THIS IS YOUR BRAIN ON...
YOUR BRAIN

BRAIN HEALTH FOR LEADERS: 89 FASCINATING THINGS ABOUT HOW YOUR BRAIN WORKS AND WHAT YOU CAN DO TO MAKE IT WORK BETTER

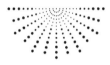

LM TAYLOR

CONTENTS

INTRODUCTION

"The human brain doesn't come with an instruction manual."

— BILL ENGVAL, AMERICAN COMEDIAN

Do you think you are in control of your decisions? You might want to rethink that assertion. Ninety-five percent of your decisions take place in your subconscious mind. This means that only five percent of the decisions we make are deliberate and consciously thought through. This can be a scary thought in a society where we feel the need to be in control of our lives. Psychology Today (2018) estimates that an average person makes about 35,000 decisions daily. Looking at these numbers, we are compelled to agree with Engval. With 35,000 decisions to make on a daily basis, we can understand why much of them occur on a subconscious level. Although we cannot change the fact that our minds make many daily decisions without conscious consideration, this does not mean we have no control over our lives or minds. We can do things to improve those subconscious decisions, even if we cannot think them through. There are ways for you to strengthen your brain and make it function more efficiently and effectively.

It can be challenging to control your life when every day is spent trying to maintain your professional life while maintaining a work-life balance. In addition, we are told to exercise and fulfill our daily duties as a husband, wife, partner, parent, guardian, or whatever other roles we might play in life. You may have experienced some difficulty in dealing with the responsibilities of life and managing your various roles. Many people ask if it is possible to accomplish this balance. The answer is yes; it is possible to live a healthy and balanced life without the accompanying stress and health complications many face.

Studies conducted by the American Institute of Stress (2022) indicate that 55 percent of Americans experience stress throughout the day, while an average of 35 percent worldwide suffer from stress regularly.

Furthermore, 94 percent of people experience stress because of their work, and 63 percent of workers in the USA feel the urge to quit their jobs to alleviate their stress. These studies also show that 57 percent of people feel paralyzed due to stress.

It is safe to say that we are facing an epidemic of stress worldwide. Unhealthy stress levels can make us feel incapable of dealing with our situations. We may think that nothing is to be done about the problem, so we carry on in our state of limbo—feeling frustrated and overwhelmed by stress and responsibility but unable to change it.

What if I told you that there is a better way of living? One that does not require you to quit your job or abandon your responsibilities and move to a remote island where no one can reach you? Although the duties of life are overwhelming, it is possible to live a meaningful life and manage our stress by protecting our brains and mental health. You can manage your various roles and responsibilities by improving and maintaining your brain health and still build a balanced life. Making this a priority will enable you to better cope with all the stresses and pressures in your life and to live a happier and more fulfilling life.

This book will help you to better understand your brain by teaching you how your brain works and how it informs the decisions you make and the emotions you feel throughout the day. It will simplify the scientific workings behind the various parts of the brain, their functions, and how they inform decision-making. Once we cover the basic physiology of the brain, we will delve into consciousness's nature and how consciousness can influence our decision-making. Furthermore, you will learn to develop essential thinking skills to help you improve your brain function and processing. You will learn how to "hack your brain" by changing how you think and react to situations. You will be equipped to take better care of your brain to ensure that you can comfortably tackle the responsibilities of life without compromising your health or well-being. This book will inform you about the vital roles that sleep, exercise, diet, and socialization have in how well our brains function. In addition, it will teach you about the effects of stress and how it can inhibit cognition. After reading this book, you should be better equipped to improve your life by caring for your brain health. Doing so will help you to think more clearly and make better decisions. Finally, you will also learn about the importance of emotional intelligence and how it can prepare you for a successful and fulfilling life. This book aims to simplify science and physiology in a way you can understand. If, at any point, there are concepts that do not make sense or you need a reminder about what it means, refer to the glossary at the end of the book.

I am by no means a medical expert either on the human brain or human behavior. Still, I have conducted extensive research on the topic to help myself understand the inner workings of my brain and manage stress in my life. I have relied on other professionals to teach me how to train my brain to live a happier, healthier life. I wrote this book to share some of my discoveries and learning about the brain with other professionals who, like me, struggle with mental performance from time to time due to stress and burnout. By learning how to look after my brain, I have been able to became far more productive and intentional with my time and energy in times of stress.

Suppose you, like me, occasionally (or more than occasionally!) struggle to keep up with the daily demands of work and other responsibilities. Yet, you would like to liberate yourself from the constant stress of twenty-first-century life. In that case, this book is written for you! By reading this book, you will equip yourself to understand your brain better in all its aspects. In addition, you can grasp how various factors and spheres of life interact with and affect the brain. Finally, and most importantly, you will empower yourself with the knowledge to take care of your brain and nurture the parts of your brain that matter.

1
THIS IS YOUR BRAIN—THIS IS WHO YOU ARE

"The brain is like a muscle. When it is in use we feel very good. Understanding is joyous."

— CARL SAGAN

This quote by Carl Sagan is a fitting way to start our journey of getting to know and understand our brains. Although your brain is an organ and not a muscle, studies have suggested that, like a muscle, your brain can be shaped and trained. Further chapters in this book will explore and explain this idea further, but first, we need to understand what the brain is, what it consists of, and how it works.

WHY DO WE EVEN NEED A BRAIN?

We all know that our brain is crucial in keeping us alive. Ask anyone to elaborate on this statement, however, and most people would not be able to explain why or even how this works. Although one of the roles of your brain is indeed keeping you alive, it is by no means the only one. You may be surprised to know that having a brain is not essential to the survival of a species. There are, in fact, many species of animals that survive without a brain, including jellyfish and starfish. These animals rely on their nervous system to process information and react. You may also have heard of people who have had portions of their brains removed and can still survive. So why, then, do we have a brain, and why do we need it?

The main reason we need a brain is to move around and function in a meaningful and purposeful way beyond basic survival instincts. A major part of our brain consists of cells called neurons. These cells are like messengers that send signals to other parts of your body to perform a certain action or task. Most of these neurons are found in the cerebellum, the part of the brain that controls movement. These neurons are responsible for everything we do—from our feelings and reactions to our movements and bodily functions like digestion.

In short, our brain allows us to perform primary functions such as breathing and digestion needed for survival. Still, it is also responsible for memory—an aspect that allows us to learn, make calculated decisions based on our experiences or develop new skills and hobbies. Furthermore, our brain plays a key part in our perceived emotions, which help us to form connections and build relationships with the people around us. Our brain, therefore, enables us to build a meaningful life based on purpose and connection. Finally, because of our brains, we can learn from our mistakes and develop healthy habits and responses to situations.

WHAT IS THE BRAIN?

The brain is an extremely complex organ comprising various parts and functions. The brain is responsible for our thoughts, senses, movements, memories, breathing, temperature regulation, and other processes that help regulate our bodies and keep them working optimally. The brain also forms part of the central nervous system, which controls our movement and forms part of our personality and intelligence. Most of our brain consists of fat, while the other parts consist of salt, water, protein, and carbohydrates.

Gray Matter and White Matter

Our central nervous system is made up of our brain and spinal cord. The central nervous system is divided into gray matter and white matter. Gray matter, scientifically known as substantial grisea, is found on the brain's outer portion and the spinal cord's inner portion. It consists mostly of neuron somas or cell bodies. Gray matter deals with the body's sensory and motor skills, thus influencing our senses and movements.

White matter, otherwise known as substantia alba, is found inside the brain and outside the spinal cord. This consists mostly of axons, which help to connect the neurons in the brain, and are wrapped in a protective covering known as myelin. Myelin is made up of lipids and proteins which not only protect axons but also serve as conductors for nerve signals. White matter helps the brain send nerve signals along the spinal cord and the rest of the body. It, therefore, helps with our reflexes and interpretation of information gathered from the gray matter parts of the brain. As the name suggests, gray matter is darker than white matter, so brain scans show darker and lighter shades.

Neurons

Below is a diagram of what a neuron looks like. The sprawling area on the left is the neuron soma found in the gray matter part of the brain, while the tail part is the axon found in the white matter. Within the axon, the little gray areas are the myelin - the covering that protects the axon. These neurons, or nerve cells, serve as messengers to communicate messages to your body. These messages contain information on what stimulus was received and how to react to the stimulus.

The Main Parts of the Brain and Their Function

The brain can be divided into three main parts: the cerebrum, brainstem, and cerebellum. Each of these parts is crucial to healthy brain function and development.

1. The Cerebrum

The cerebrum is the largest part of the brain, making up roughly 85% of the brain's total weight. It can be found in the front part of the brain and consists of gray and white matter. The cerebrum is vital to both movement and temperature regulation in the body. Still, it contributes to several other important higher-order functions such as speech, thought processes, emotional development, sensory functions, and the ability to learn.

The gray matter in the cerebrum is known as the cerebral cortex, which accounts for roughly half of your brain mass. The cerebral cortex is divided into two halves, known as the right hemisphere, which controls the right side of the body, and the left hemisphere, which controls the left side. These two hemispheres meet in the interhemispheric fissure or the medial longitudinal fissure. The two hemispheres communicate through the white matter in the center of the cerebrum using nerve pathways called the corpus callosum, which is found in the center of the cerebrum.

2. Brainstem

The brainstem is a small part at the bottom of your brain that forms part of your central nervous system and connects your cerebrum to your spinal cord. The brainstem is divided into three parts. Firstly, the midbrain, scientifically known as the mesencephalon, helps to control your eye movements and enables other movements and coordination. Secondly, the pons is the middle part of the brainstem and connects the midbrain with the medulla. This area is responsible for facial movements, expression, hearing, and balance. Finally, the medulla is found at the bottom of the brainstem and connects the brain to the spinal cord. The medulla is responsible for many important bodily functions, such as regulating breathing, heart rate, blood flow, oxygen and carbon dioxide, and reflexive movements.

3. Cerebellum

The cerebellum is found at the back of the brain. It is a Latin word meaning "little brain" and is roughly the size of a fist. Like the cerebral cortex, this part of the brain is divided into two parts. The outer part of the cerebellum contains neurons. In contrast, the inner part communicates with the cerebral cortex to coordinate muscle movement and manage posture and balance. Scientists are still making discoveries and inquiries about the cerebellum, and many unanswered questions relate to its function. Still, the functions discussed here are proven and accepted as factually accurate.

Damage to any of these brain parts can prove catastrophic, as they all play a vital role in controlling and regulating essential daily functions and very important higher-order capabilities.

Meninges

The meninges are three protective layers surrounding and protecting the brain and brainstem.

1. The dura mater is the thick, outermost layer of the meninges located under the skull, or cranium. It consists of two layers—the periosteal layer and the meningeal layer. The spaces between these two layers allow veins and arteries to supply blood flow to and from the brain.

2. The arachnoid consists of a very thin, almost web-like, layer of connective tissue. The purpose of connective tissue is to connect and provide support and structure to other parts of the body. This layer does not contain nerves or blood vessels. Instead, the cerebrospinal fluid is found under this layer that helps to cushion the central nervous system—the brain and the spinal cord. The cerebrospinal fluid also helps to filter out impurities to protect the central nervous system.

3. The pia mater is another thin layer filled with veins and arteries on top of the central nervous system.

Lobes of the Brain

The cerebral cortex is divided into four sections, or lobes, each performing a different function.

1. The frontal lobe is the largest of the four sections at the front of the brain. This part is concerned mostly with personality, movement, and decision-making processes. It is also associated with smell and speech abilities.

2. The parietal lobe is in the middle of the brain and involves sensory and spatial processes. For example,

this is where the brain identifies and processes pain stimuli and touch. This part of the brain also helps in understanding and interpreting spoken language.

3. The temporal lobe is found on the bottom side of the brain. This section plays a role in forming and retaining short-term memory and recognizing speech and rhythms. It also plays some part in helping us recognize different smells. Since this part of the brain is involved in short-term memory, it is also involved in helping us form memories.

4. The occipital lobe is found in the back of the brain and primarily involves vision and sight processing. Thus, the occipital lobe helps us to identify and process visual information.

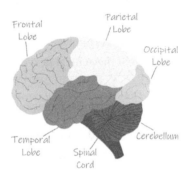

Deeper Structures Within the Brain

The Pituitary Gland

The pituitary gland, also known as the "master gland," is a small, pea-sized structure located at the base of the brain behind the bridge of the nose. The pituitary gland controls the function of other glands in the body, thus regulating the hormones released into other body parts.

Hypothalamus

The hypothalamus is found above the pituitary gland and communicates chemical messages to the pituitary to control it. The hypothalamus helps to control body temperature, sleeping patterns, and hunger and thirst. It also contributes to memory formation and emotions.

Amygdala

The amygdala is found under each of the brain's hemispheres in the form of small, almond-shaped bodies. This forms a part of the brain that helps to control and regulate emotion and memory. It also involves stress responses, such as the infamous "fight-or-flight." This part of the brain helps us to process information and make a decision on how to react.

Hippocampus

This is found in the temporal lobe and is part of a structure called the hippocampal formation. This part of the brain also plays a role in our fight-or-flight response and helps with memory formation and recall.

Pineal Gland

This gland is found within the brain and plays a role in releasing melanin, responding to light and dark, and regulating our sleep-wake cycles and circadian rhythms: the physical, behavioral, and mental changes that we go through within a 24-hour day.

Ventricles and Cerebrospinal Fluid

Within our brain, four areas with open passageways lead into the spine's center and below the meninges' arachnoid layer. These are known as ventricles, and they produce cerebrospinal fluid, which circulates between the ventricles and spinal cord and between the meninges. This fluid helps to protect the central nervous system and flushes out impurities. It also helps to deliver important nutrients.

Blood Supply to the Brain

The vertebral and carotid arteries are the two blood vessels that supply blood and oxygen to the brain. Carotid arteries can be divided into internal and external carotid arteries. External carotid arteries are found on the sides of the neck. This is usually where people place their fingers when checking for a pulse. Internal carotids extend into the skull and help to circulate blood flow into the front part of the brain. Vertebral arteries travel along the spinal column and into the skull. These arteries form basilar arteries, where they join together and supply blood to the back part of the brain. A third cluster is formed, known as the circle of Willis. This circle consists of blood vessels near the base of the brain that forms a loop that connects the main arteries and helps supply blood from the front of the brain to the back. This system also establishes a connection between arterial systems to help them communicate with each other.

Cranial Nerves

Cranial nerves are nerves that are found within the cranium or skull. Twelve nerves are found in the skull, each of which serves a specific function.

1. The olfactory nerve is responsible for the sense of smell.
2. The optic nerve controls eyesight.
3. The oculomotor nerve is responsible for eye movement and originates where the midbrain and pons meet.
4. The trochlear nerve controls the muscles in the eye and stems from the midbrain.
5. The trigeminal nerve is the biggest of the cranial nerves. It controls the senses and motor function or movement. This nerve originates from the pons.
6. The abducens nerve supplies nerves to some of the muscles found in the eye.
7. The facial nerve controls facial movements, taste, and some glandular functions.
8. The vestibulocochlear nerve controls balance and hearing.
9. The glossopharyngeal nerve controls ear and throat movement as well as taste.
10. The vagus nerve is responsible for sensation in the ear and the digestive system. It also controls movement in the throat, heart, and digestive system.
11. The accessory nerve supplies nerves to certain head, shoulders, and neck muscles.
12. The hypoglossal nerve enables movement in the tongue.

The olfactory and optic nerves are located in the cerebrum, and the rest originate in the brainstem.

HUMAN CONSCIOUSNESS—THE MOST IMPORTANT FUNCTION OF THE BRAIN

Most animals, like humans, have brains that help them function and survive. But, although these animals have brains, they lack human consciousness. Consciousness is one of the things that sets us apart from other mammals and animals. It is one of the brain's most important functions that allow us to make decisions, feel empathy, and learn from our mistakes.

What Is Consciousness?

Consciousness is a very abstract concept but can be summed up as having awareness; of ourselves and the world around us. Some synonyms of consciousness include awareness, alertness, and responsiveness. Being conscious means being aware of and able to process our thoughts, emotions, memories, and what is happening in our environment. Every person's consciousness differs based on their experiences. This enables us to process information more effectively, prioritize tasks and information, adapt to new environments and situations, and make conscious decisions.

Our conscious state is still a mystery to many scientists. Three important dimensions or areas of consciousness may be useful in explaining how and why the brain can create or enable consciousness. The first aspect is wakefulness or physical arousal. This involves being physically awake or present in a situation, meaning that we are not unconscious. The second aspect involves being mentally present and having conscious thoughts, perceptions, or emotions. Thus, being able to consciously think. The third important aspect of consciousness involves being conscious in our senses— thus being able to assimilate experiences using information acquired through our senses.

When we sleep, our state of consciousness is altered but not absent. One such example is during the rapid eye movement (REM) sleep cycle; dreams are most likely to occur when we are in the deepest form of sleep. Drugs and hallucinogens can also alter our state of consciousness. Although we receive the same stimuli or information, we interpret and organize that information differently due to our altered consciousness.

Studies suggest that consciousness is directly related to the connectivity between different brain parts. When conscious-ness is chemically altered, these connections are shown to have been broken; thus, the brain cannot communicate messages clearly to the rest of the body.

Consciousness and the Brain

Four fundamentals can be used in describing and under-standing consciousness.

1. Conscious content is the term used to describe the most basic form of consciousness, in other words, a basic awareness of one's senses. Thus, a memory, a sight, or a smell might classify as conscious content.

2. A conscious field comprises a collection of conscious contents that occur in a single moment. Thus, everything that a person experiences or feels in a particular moment forms a conscious field. For example, when I am sitting at my desk, I may experience the smell of my coffee, the feel of my keyboard beneath my fingers, the roughness of the carpet under my bare feet, and the sense of a slight breeze coming through the window.

3. The third fundamental is accepting that not all brain processes are part of consciousness. For example, an impulse or reflexive reaction results from signals sent via the brain to trigger a response. There is no conscious effort or thought involved. Thus, consciousness is only involved in a subset of experiences and processes of the brain.

4. Finally, conscious contents trigger certain brain processes and sometimes behaviors. The more conscious contents that are presented simultaneously, the more advanced our reactions and abilities to make conscious decisions become. Consider, for example, a person buying a cold sugary drink on a hot day. In isolation, that cold drink tastes delicious and helps to cool you down. However, when paired with the thought that sugary drinks can cause diabetes, your reaction changes, and you might refrain from such indulgences.

These four fundamentals help us to better understand consciousness and how it works. We have experiences, and these experiences and stimuli do not occur in isolation. Not

all experiences and reactions involve consciousness; a bigger collection of conscious contents leads to more informed and conscious decision-making.

The Purpose of Consciousness

According to Eysenck & Keane (2015), consciousness has five main functions:

- Consciousness allows us to perceive our environment to make sense of everything.
- It also allows us to communicate and engage with people around us and understand their thoughts and emotions.
- Consciousness is important in determining our actions and reactions.
- It allows us to think about other things outside of the present that can affect us in the future.
- Finally, consciousness allows us to consider and synthesize various types and sources of information to determine what is happening.

States and Functions of the Conscious Mind

Three commonly accepted states of the conscious mind determine the level of consciousness we experience and how we process information. Reflecting consciousness is the first and most basic state of consciousness. In this state of consciousness, we may retain information without much thought or analysis. Analytical consciousness is the next level when information is processed and analyzed to determine whether it should be retained. Finally, transcendentalism is the highest form of consciousness, in which a person becomes truly aware and critical of the information that passes through his or her mind. This involves critical and creative thinking and even metacognition—thinking about our thoughts.

In addition to the three states of consciousness, the conscious mind has five functions. These functions are sometimes determined by the situation in which consciousness is practiced.

1. Reflection, as mentioned previously, occurs when information is taken in and processed without much thought or critical analysis. This can often lead to irrational emotions like anxiety or love at first sight.

2. Filtration is the process by which information is sorted, knowingly or unknowingly, and some are discarded. A good example of unintentional filtration is when someone speaks to you while doing something else. You may hear the person's voice, and you acknowledge their voice. Still, while focusing on the task you are completing, that information is discarded. You have no recall of what the person was saying. Filtration can be used intentionally to ward off negative or unwanted thoughts.

3. Differentiation occurs when your mind attempts to provide feedback. Again, this is related to metathinking, as certain thoughts or questions may arise while you are conversing. Your mind will then search for the answer to those questions, or prompt

you to find the answer if the information is unavailable in your memory archives.

4. Imagination involves a higher level of creative thinking. This process involves manifesting subconscious information into reality. This imagination becomes reality for the person whose mind is involved but may not be the reality to others.

5. Finally, transcendence is the highest form of consciousness. This stage of consciousness occurs when the mind can perform higher-order thinking processes without much effort, thus being in a constant state of awareness. This means that skills such as reflection, filtration, and critical thinking happen automatically.

EVOLUTION OF THE BRAIN

The brain has evolved and developed over time and among different species. The theory of evolution dictates that human beings have developed and transcended from certain species of prehistoric apes, and it is widely accepted that humans are far more intelligent and developed than other animals and mammals. People consider brain size, the cerebral and prefrontal cortex development, and the level of encephalization—the development and complexity of the brain—to be indicators of such intelligence. However, Gerhard Roth (2005) suggests that a better indicator of intelligence is the number of neurons in our cerebral cortex and how quickly they can convey messages between the brain and other parts of the body. Thus, he suggests that humans are more intelligent because our cerebral cortex has more neurons and better conductivity.

INTERESTING FACTS ABOUT THE HUMAN BRAIN

If this chapter has shown us anything, the brain is severely complex and intricately designed. The human brain is so complex that parts of it have yet to be understood. Here are a few facts on the brain, as cited by Lewis and Taylor (2021), that might help you understand it better or even want to read more about it.

The human brain weighs roughly 3 pounds and makes up about two percent of the human body. Furthermore, male brains are, on average, about ten percent larger than female brains. However, we have learned that this does not inherently make them more intelligent. The brain has roughly 86 billion neurons and the same amount of non-neuron cells. Furthermore, contrary to popular belief, the brain cannot multitask. It is physically impossible. Rather, what we consider multitasking is the ability to quickly switch between tasks. Cleveland Clinic (2022) suggests that multitasking is ineffective as it causes a division in your attention, thus causing us to lose effectiveness and focus on the task in question.

Regarding brain development and growth, our brain size triples in the first year of life and completes its growth at age 25. This does not mean the brain is at its full potential at this age, as we will learn throughout this book.

The human brain can generate enough electricity to power a small light bulb.

These few facts about the brain show just how much of the brain we truly understand—or do not understand. So now that we have met the brain and learned some of the important aspects of the brain and its functions, we can delve into how the brain changes when we start to use it.

2
LEARNING AND THE BRAIN

"Education isn't just about feeding the brain. Art and music feed the heart and soul."

— JULIE GARWOOD

I think a reasonable period would generally agree with Julie. However, education and learning play a tremendous role in shaping the brain and changing our thinking. It is about far more than merely retaining and remembering information. Rather, learning changes the brain's physical structure and determines how we learn and retain information and even how we respond to the information we learn.

Furthermore, as Julie Garwood suggests in her quote, music can also affect the brain and how it responds. These influences can be positive or negative depending on how we use them. The best and highest form of learning is metacognition, which happens when we start to think about how we think rather than merely accepting and retaining the information we hear and see. When we learn to inquire into our own learning, we can begin to understand our influence over our brain and its development.

NEUROPLASTICITY

Neuroplasticity refers to our brain's ability to change physically. Every time we learn something new and information is retained, the physical structure of our brain changes. Thus, when we say that experience molds or shapes a person, we mean so in the physical sense and metaphorically. Although our brains physically stop growing at the age of 25, our brain changes and adapts throughout our life based on our experiences. Thus, brain development never truly stops.

In the first chapter, you learned about the importance of neurons in communicating signals to the rest of the body, which evokes a response or reaction. These connections, or synapses, can change throughout our life as we learn and retain information. This is where consciousness becomes important, shaping our reactions and thought processes. This leads to long-term potentiation, the constant strengthening of existing connections, and synaptogenesis, which forms new connections. When we link this to what I have said about consciousness, brain connections are strengthened when multiple neurons are fired simultaneously, thus improving intelligence.

The hippocampus is the only region in the brain where neurons are newly generated through neurogenesis. As we know, the hippocampus plays an important role in memory and learning. Thus, it is through learning and remembering that our brain changes and we develop.

We can conclude that intelligence is not determined at birth but can be developed through memory and learning by long-term potentiation. Secondly, learning happens automatically throughout our lives, but deliberate learning may prove more effective in improving our cognitive function. Thus, higher-order thinking and meaningful learning can shape our brains to help them function better and react more effectively.

HOW DOES LEARNING PROGRAM THE BRAIN?

The brain is very similar to a computer in that it can be programmed to run certain processes, and these processes can change. This is done through learning. Just as a computer runs certain problems through a preset circuit to determine an outcome, the brain is wired to run information through a circuit before determining a reaction or coming to a conclusion. Learning can change the course of this circuit.

The brain contains what are known as dendritic spines. These little bubbles form on the dendrites—the tree-like part of the neuron. The size and number of these dendritic spines change in response to the formation of memories or the act of learning taking place. When this happens, information is stored within the dendritic spines. Thus, when a particular topic of learning arises in the future, these dendritic spines can activate the recall of information retained before the encounter. Learning and memory formation thus occurs with a consistent and collective enhancement of these dendritic spines. The more information is gathered on a particular topic or experience, the better the future outcome, as more information is available for analysis when a similar issue arises. In addition, the collective enhancement of dendritic spines strengthens the connections between neurons, thus improving intelligence and cognition. Ultimately, the more information we have retained about a certain experience or topic, the more cells clump together to assimilate the information. This is where learning becomes evident.

LANGUAGE AND THE BRAIN

Language is a complex and intricate discipline that requires multidisciplinary understanding. Learning a new language does not merely involve remembering the correct words for certain concepts; it also requires understanding the language conventions of different races and cultures. While communication between animals is merely repetitive and functional, human language is complex in that it allows for translating deeper thoughts and emotions. It also allows the speaker to communicate information regarding their surroundings, other objects, and certain actions.

Learning a new language can change the way that our brain works as well as the physical structure of our brain. Being bilingual or multilingual proves useful for communication and seems to improve our brain functioning and intelligence significantly. It was discovered that bilingual people have more neurons and dendrites compared to people who know only one language. They also seem to have improved connectivity between their neurons, thus indicating higher levels of intelligence and cognition. Although this connection is stronger in people who grew up bilingual, learning a new language can still benefit your brain health, regardless of age. Remember that connections between neurons can be strengthened throughout life thanks to neuroplasticity. Therefore, it is never too late to think about learning a new language - and reaping its benefits.

Language is a powerful learning and development tool because it requires more than mere recall. Since different languages have their own grammatical rules, and since language is such a complex thing, it requires critical thinking and synthesis of  information, as it requires you to build on prior knowledge and learning. There are several benefits to learning a new language. Firstly, Spence (2022) states that most studies on the effects of language learning on academic performance show that learners who study a second language perform better academically than those who do not. Secondly, learners who study a second language show a lengthened attention span and improved focus. This leads to point three, which indicates that those who learn a second language have a more powerful memory, as language learning requires understanding and memorizing various complex grammatical rules and conventions. The fourth, more obvious advantage of learning a new language is improved communication skills. Those who have learned two or more languages can communicate with more people using the varied languages, communicate better overall, and are more adept at showing compassion. Finally, people who have learned two or more languages indicate higher creativity and creative problem-solving levels. This is most likely due to the complexity of language, which requires studying, translation, and differentiating between languages.

MUSIC AND THE BRAIN

Music has a very clear and evident effect on the brain, and it can be seen in how songs get stuck in your head, or you can't help but tap your feet to the beat of a song or sway to its rhythms. So we have a very clear physical response to music and rhythms. But, still, there is also a neurological response that takes place.

Many of us listen to music as a way of improving our mood. Listening to certain types of music releases dopamine and serotonin—"feel good" hormones—into our bodies. These hormones help to increase our mood. Furthermore, when you feel stressed, listening to calming music can decrease adrenaline and cortisol—hormones that cause stress. Similarly, listening to sad music when you feel depressed can worsen your symptoms and alter your mood. This indicates that we need to be careful of the music we listen to, as it can directly impact our mood and even our mental health.

In the same way, however, we can also use music deliberately to improve our mental health. Music is not only related to our moods. It has been shown to impact physical and mental health as well. Music has been shown to increase blood flow, which helps to reduce stress and anxiety, lower blood pressure, and alleviate pain. Furthermore, it has also been shown to improve sleep quality. In fact, in some cases, music has been used as a cure for insomnia. Interestingly, playing music during mealtimes also seems to slow down eating, which helps people to eat less. Because music releases feel-good hormones, music can also improve performance during exercise.

In terms of focus and productivity in a working environment, music can improve productivity or provide distraction, depending on the environment. Music can be helpful in a busy and noisy environment, as it drowns out distracting noises and conversation. In these cases, it is best to listen to music without lyrics, as it will limit our brains' focus on the music. As discussed previously, multitasking causes a split in the brain's attention, thus limiting the brain's ability to focus on the task being completed. Therefore, it is better to not listen to music in a quiet environment where you can focus. In these cases, it is unnecessary to listen to music, as this serves as an added distraction, unnecessarily splitting your brain's focus and limiting your productivity.

Music can also be used to influence our behaviors. It is common knowledge that music is a big part of the marketing industry. In shops and restaurants where fast-paced music is played, people generally shop or eat much faster, thus allowing new customers to come in and increasing the business's revenue. The outcome is more effective if this music is played at a louder volume. Another example of this is what is known as the "Manilow Effect," wherein shops would play Barry Manilow's music in their shops as a method of getting teenagers to linger for a much shorter period and move on faster.

Thus, music can tremendously impact our mood, concentration, and physical and mental health. This should alert you to how important it is to be aware of the music we are listening to and its effect on our brains. Now that you know its influence, consider using music more deliberately to target your low moods and lapses in productivity. Use its influence to your advantage.

HOW THE BRAIN PROCESSES LEARNING

Have you ever felt confused while looking at an optical illusion or been overwhelmed by too many sounds and noises? Our brain categorizes what we see, feel, hear, and experience. When faced with these overwhelming situations, our brain's ability to organize is confused. The brain's categorization of inputs enables us to learn, retain, and recall information as and when necessary. It seems that the key to learning and cognition lies in visual categorization. During visual categorization, neurons in the parietal and prefrontal cortices are engaged, and it is their function to encode and sort visual information. The parietal and prefrontal cortices are the areas involved in higher-order levels of cognition.

When we are engaged in lower-level learning, like differentiating between objects or patterns, there is no real retention of information. However, visual categorization takes place if we are engaged in higher-order learning. Therefore, the primary way our brain can synthesize learning is through visual categorization, in which what we see is categorized and stored for future reference. When we see these or similar objects in the future, the information is instantly available to judge what we are seeing or experiencing and provide more information on how we should respond.

METACOGNITION

In previous chapters of this book, I have referred to metacognition as a form of higher-order thinking. Metacognition is a form of thinking about thinking. It involves being aware of how we think and why we think a certain way so we are better able to improve our cognitive skills. By reading this book, you improve your metacognitive abilities by learning how the brain works and reacts in certain situations. For example, suppose you know how the brain forms memories and synthesizes information. In that case, you will be better able to improve your learning abilities by focusing on the methods that best promote higher-order learning. You have read, for example, that multitasking is ineffective. Thus, to improve your learning and productivity, you may refrain from multitasking and plan your day and learn activities by focusing on one task.

Metacognition is a key factor in becoming an independent learner. When you understand how your brain works and how learning takes place, having someone facilitate learning for you is no longer necessary. This form of thinking involves self-reflection—thinking about what you have learned and how it can add value to your life. It requires setting goals and holding yourself accountable to those goals. Finally, it requires self-evaluation—assessing your learning and whether you are being effective or productive in the learning process.

Metacognition does not only involve learning in a formal sense. It can also be a very useful tool regarding our thoughts and reactions. If we are aware of how our brain works, we are also better able to maintain our mental health and evaluate how we feel and how to respond based on our emotions. If you know, for example, that certain activities of certain types of music make you feel sad or depressed, you can better look after yourself by avoiding these activities. In the same way, if you know that certain comments or people provoke a reaction from you, then metacognition allows us to evaluate why we react in this way and how better to react in the future. Essentially, we can identify our biases through metacognition. Thus, metacognition will help us not only to learn better but also to help us improve our reactions and respond more constructively and healthily.

Here is a personal example related to metacognition. If you supervise people, or otherwise hold some sort of leadership me you likely have developed or eventually tain personality preferences for the people I have a particular loathing for laziness. I ....her work with someone with no relavent experience but a strong work ethic than someone who tends toward laziness. Both individuals may actually produce the same amount of work, but it just gets my hackles up, so to speak, when someone is lazy and doesn't raise to their potential for that reason. But, because I now <u>know</u> that I have this bias, I can stop myself from making rash judgements and decisions about individuals solely based on my bias. Because laziness is so abhorrent to me, and by that I mean it elicits a strong emotional response, sometimes I see laziness in someone that really isn't there. There are other reasons that a particular project is behind, that a certain task remains unfinished week after week, and so on. If I had not come to recognize my own bias in this area, I could have lost out on what have become some wonderful and meaningful professional relationships just because of my own misperceptions based on a personal bias.

Now that you understand how learning takes place and affects the brain, it is important to understand how we can care for ourselves and look after our brain health.

3
BRAIN HEALTH

Has your brain ever felt foggy or disconnected from reality? Have you found yourself wandering through your day aimlessly and then struggling to fall asleep, only to wake up exhausted the next day? This happens when we do not look after our mental health. The term mental health has been so associated with mental disorders and mental illnesses that we have been led to believe that our mental health is fine as long as we have not been diagnosed with mental illness. However, brain fog and exhaustion indicate we have been neglecting our brain health. Having a healthy brain does not simply require learning consistently. Rather, certain important aspects are essential to maintaining a healthy brain.

"A well-spent day brings happy sleep."

— LEONARDO DA VINCI

Although this may seem like an oversimplified statement, it holds significant truth. Suppose we are deliberate in how we spend our days. In that case, we will rest better at night as we feel more fulfilled and satisfied with our lives and our decisions throughout the day. This is very important, as sleep is also essential for better brain function. Suppose we plan our days and deliberate about the activities we engage in throughout the day. In that case, we can maintain mental health and create a more fulfilling and meaningful life. This does not mean we need to plan out daily, minute by minute. It also does not mean that every day should be productive in terms of work that needs to be done. Resting is also important, and it can also be productive. Rather, it means being deliberate and conscious in whatever we do and including activities that promote brain health throughout the week.

BRAIN EXERCISES TO PROMOTE MENTAL HEALTH

Mental health and brain development can be managed and improved by looking after our brains. Certain brain exercises can be done to improve our mental sharpness and develop our brain to function better daily. Doing these exercises can help you improve your memory, concentration, and focus, thus helping you perform tasks more effectively and make time for other meaningful tasks and activities. Brain exercises can also reduce the risk of developing neurological diseases such as Alzheimer's and Dementia. We have already discussed how learning a new language or listening to music can improve mental health. Here are some other activities and exercises that can help you to improve and maintain brain health.

1. Jigsaw puzzles may not seem like a brain game, but these can be very beneficial to improve brain development. Building a puzzle can significantly strengthen your brain and help to maintain your brain, as it uses various cognitive functions simultaneously.

2. Card games can also contribute to brain development. Card games are stimulating and help with improving memory and concentration skills.

3. Do something that builds your vocabulary. Learning new words and developing your vocabulary involves visual and auditory processes, thus strengthening your brain. Try to learn at least one new word a day, write the definition down, and try to use this new word as often as possible.

4. Dancing may seem like more of a physical than cognitive activity, but learning new dance moves helps to improve brain speed and memory. It is, therefore, both physically and mentally advantageous. Whether you love dancing or have two left feet, this can help develop your cognitive function. With the technology and access available today, you do not need to attend a dancing class to do this. Simply go to YouTube and find a video that teaches a new dance—your brain will thank you!

5. Engaging in activities involving all your senses can also benefit brain health. This can involve baking, visiting a restaurant you have always wanted to visit,

or going to a market. This forces us to use sight, smell, touch, hearing, and tasting simultaneously and encourages brain development as the brain processes more information simultaneously.

6. Learning a new skill is another great way to train your brain, as it actively involves learning and synthesizing information. Doing so strengthens the connections between neurons in our brain, and we know, based on what was discussed in chapter two, that stronger brain connections improve intelligence.

7. If you are already skilled in a certain task or activity, teaching a skill to someone else can benefit your brain. This can be anything from playing an instrument to cooking or tutoring a subject. Teaching someone else allows us to analyze information to explain concepts and correct mistakes and misconceptions.

8. Alternating your route or changing your routine can help you to change your thinking and take in new information, thus helping the brain develop.

9. Meditation has been proven to improve consciousness and help to calm you down. Meditation forces us to breathe slowly, releasing stress and slowing our heart rate. As little as five minutes of meditation can be beneficial to not only your mental but also your physical health.

10. Focusing on others instead of ourselves can be surprisingly refreshing. Constantly focusing on yourself and your own issues can be detrimental to your health, as it can become easy to focus only on the negative. Instead, take note of four details of

someone else—the color of their hair, the clothes they are wearing, or their face shape. This improves our awareness of the details around us and helps us to remember things more easily.

These are only a few examples of things that can improve our brain health and development. Improving our brain health does not always have to involve formal learning environments. Instead, we can adopt new habits and hobbies that we enjoy and spend a few minutes developing those every day or just a few times a week.

LIFESTYLE CHANGES TO ENSURE GOOD BRAIN HEALTH

Managing and maintaining our mental health should not only happen when we notice our health faltering. Maintaining good brain health should be a part of our daily lives, and we should be aware of our brain health when planning our days and the activities that need to be completed. Often, we engage in harmful activities and habits as a coping mechanism or because they "feel good" and only try to change them once we notice our health suffering. We often think of these habits only regarding their impact on physical health. However, these habits and activities can have some serious long-term effects on our mental health, even if we change them. There are some habits or lifestyle choices you may not have known are harmful to your mental health.

Exercise is not only good for maintaining physical health but can improve brain health as well. Increased blood flow means the brain can function better and communicate information faster. Exercise has also shown a correlation with memory performance. Maintaining a healthy diet is crucial to maintaining brain health. There are, in fact, some foods that have been identified as "brain-boosting foods" due to their nutrients that boost mental performance. Unhealthy foods that affect your body also affect your brain, as they can affect blood flow, which decreases the effectiveness of your brain. Practicing mindfulness can help to reduce stress and anxiety and also helps us to practice metacognition, thus improving brain function. Overall, anything that is detrimental to your physical health will inadvertently affect your mental health as well. If you want to maintain good brain health, you must start looking after your physical health as the two are intricately connected.

SLEEP AND THE BRAIN

Sleep almost seems like a luxury in our current society, with our busy schedules and our lives demanding so much of our time and attention. On the contrary, sleep is crucial to physical and mental health. Getting enough sleep is essential for our body and brain to function optimally. Sleeping serves several purposes in the body and is not only necessary for resting.

Getting the necessary amount of sleep allows our brains to regulate our emotions more effectively, making us less prone to emotional outbursts and reactivity. On the other hand, a lack of sleep makes us far more reactive to emotional stimuli, which is when we overreact to seemingly trivial situations.

This can tremendously impact our mental health, as sleep deprivation exposes us to emotional disorders like depression or anxiety. Due to the same disconnect in emotional regulation, our relationships with others will also suffer. We cannot regulate our reactions and may have difficulty showing empathy and emotional connection. Getting enough sleep helps us empathize better, thus identifying others' emotional states based on their facial expressions.

Furthermore, better sleep can help to reduce stress and anxiety, which is much better for overall health. Better emotional regulation also means that we do not experience emotions as intently, thus improving overall satisfaction and reducing the effects of experiencing an emotional overload. Sleep deprivation has been linked to increased risk for heart disease, strokes, and obesity.

Sleep is intricately linked to learning and cognitive functions related to learning. Getting enough sleep is linked to an improved ability to store information for short-term memory and transfer important information to long-term storage. Thus, people who do not get enough sleep may struggle to synthesize and remember information. This indicates why people with sleep deprivation have so much difficulty remembering information and recalling memories or conversations. It is important to note that sleep cannot be "caught up" per se. In other words, if you sleep very little during the week, sleeping for ten to twelve hours over the weekend will not counteract the effects of sleep deprivation accumulated during the week. Rather, healthy sleeping patterns should be practiced consistently for the brain to function optimally. Not only do we benefit from sleep, but dreams can also play an important role in brain function.

What Are Dreams and Why Do We Dream?

Dreams are the thoughts, images, or feelings that we experience in a state of sleep. They occur most often during the sleeping cycle's REM (rapid eye movement) phase. Typically, dreams take place from a first-person perspective. In other words, the dreamer experiences the dream as though they are in it. Dreams are most often involuntary and can sometimes be incoherent or illogical. Dreams often involve and evoke strong emotions, incorporating elements of real life that the dreamer may have seen or experienced. This includes other people in the dream, as these faces often represent people seen or interacted with in real life.

During the REM phase, the stress and anxiety hormone noradrenaline is non-existent. Thus, we experience no stress or anxiety during this sleep cycle phase. Simultaneously, memories and experiences are resurfaced during REM. Thus, we can then relive memories and experiences that may have happened during the day without experiencing the worry of the moment. This allows us to work through these memories without the added stress of the environment, removing the intensity of the emotion we may have felt at the moment. Dr. Matthew Walker addresses this function when he states that: "It's said that time heals all wounds, but my research suggests that time spent in dream sleep is what heals."

Dreaming also helps to improve creativity and complex problem-solving. This is clear when we consider the content of our dreams. Dreams are often made up of things we have seen and experienced, and dreams are creative scenarios that play out in real-time. Therefore, our brain formulates these scenarios and consecutive scenarios as the dream plays out, thus developing the creative and problem-solving areas of the brain.

I personally find all of this information about dreams quite interesting, but the single most amazing thing that I have learned about sleep, dreams, and the human brain has to do with learning. When we sleep, our brains don't. Our brains don't "rest" while we sleep. In layman's terms, our brains essentially organize, categorize, and store the information and experiences from the day while we sleep, retaining the data; i.e., learning. The human brain sorts through this information and "stores", or records similar data and experiences together with other past experiences and learned information that is similar to the new information. Visually, you can think of it as the brain filing away data points in similar file folders inside your head. That is why you sometimes dream of some person or experience from you past for seemingly no logical reason - something about a piece of information or experience from today is similar enough to an experience from the past that your brain is storing that information in the same spot in your brain, which can trigger memories of a past experience in your unconscious dreaming state.

If you don't get enough sleep, your brain simply cannot keep up with the workload of sorting and storing the information that you took in that day, which impairs your ability to learn.

This information is useful and important, but you may have trouble sleeping and thus not understand how to benefit. There are a few things that you can do to improve your sleep to benefit effectively. Firstly, it is important to ensure that your room is dark within two hours of sleep and that no bright light sources can affect your sleep. Stop all screen time two hours before you go to sleep, including cell phones, computers, and televisions. These can affect your sleep and make falling asleep more difficult. Secondly, a consistent sleep schedule is important for effective sleep. This helps your body to prepare for bedtime naturally, as it can be predicted based on a regular schedule. Try to go to sleep and wake up at the same time every day. This may take some time, but it will be more beneficial in the long term. Keep your house cool at night. A lower temperature helps signal the brain that it is time to sleep and helps you fall asleep faster. Finally, refrain from drinking alcohol or caffeine late in the day or at night. These can interfere with sleep quality. If you struggle to fall asleep or suffer from insomnia, it might help you not to spend time in bed while awake. Our brain forms connections with the spaces we are in. Thus, only being on your bed when you are sleeping will help signal the brain that it is time to sleep when you go to bed. If you lay awake at night in your bed, move to another room or a chair and read a book under a dim light until you feel sleepy, then return to bed.

EXERCISE AND BRAIN HEALTH

I have mentioned previously that exercising can be important and beneficial to brain health. Exercise can help improve cognition and memory and contribute to mental health. Furthermore, it can help to prevent neurological disorders and mental illnesses. Exercising increases blood flow throughout the body, which improves mental performance and allows the brain to work faster and more efficiently. Exercise also helps to reduce stress as it drops stress hormones, thus providing mental clarity and improving cognitive function. Exercise releases endorphins in the body, which improves our mood and helps us feel revitalized. It increases our energy levels, which improves focus and lengthens our attention span. It also helps to decrease brain fog as blood circulation and cognitive functioning are improved.

Exercise has been found to increase neuron production in the brain, thus speeding up the communication process between the brain and the body. In addition, exercise improves mental clarity, thus helping us to deal better and more rationally with our emotions. When we engage in physical activity, our brain releases four important chemicals. The first is the Brain-Derived Neurotrophic Factor (BNDF), which serves as a fertilizer for neurons, promoting the survival and growth of neurons in the brain. Secondly, it also promotes the release of serotonin, a hormone that regulates moods. Serotonin can help the body regulate anxiety and create a feeling of happiness. This will increase your motivation and willpower when exercising or completing daily tasks. Norepinephrine is the third chemical it releases, which controls your body's fight-or-flight response. As a result, you may experience an increased heart rate, blood flow, and, most importantly, a boost in your energy levels. Thus, releasing norepinephrine will boost your energy levels and improve your concentration. The final hormone released during exercise is dopamine—the ultimate feel-good hormone. Dopamine is mostly associated with pleasure and can provide focus and motivation and improve decision-making. Releasing these hormones leads to improved mood and energy boosts after exercise.

The amount of exercise required and the intensity thereof will vary based on your age and your ultimate goal. It may be a good idea to consult a physician or coach if you want to pursue new physical goals. However, the important thing is to remain active as much as possible throughout the week. Remember that exercise does not only involve intensive cardio or weight-lifting exercises. There are many forms of exercise, some more vigorous than others, and each of these exercises has its benefits. In addition, there are different types of exercises that you can do to experience the cognitive benefits.

Exercises such as yoga, tai chi, and aerobic classes are best to reduce brain fog and improve concentration. You may consider aerobics, walking, and cycling for optimal memory performance. Suppose you want to work on improving the blood circulation in your body. In that case, you need to engage in more cardio activities. These include running, walking, cycling, swimming, skipping rope, or kickboxing. Yoga is best for relieving stress and anxiety, as it requires a lot of concentration and mindfulness. Finally, to relieve depression, consider aerobics or resistance training, as these encourage perseverance and boost motivation.

Quite a bit of science is backing the health benefits of exercise on the brain. I will attempt to simplify them so you can understand how exercise impacts your brain. All of the scientific evidence discussed here was taken from an article by Cotman and Berchtold (2002). All evidence used to support their findings was gathered in animal experimentation. According to them, regular physical exercise lowers the risk of developing Alzheimer's and dementia. This is because exercise prolongs the survival and production of neurons and decreases insulin resistance. It helps to improve learning ability and even helps to maintain cognitive functioning in old age. Their article supports the earlier assertion that BDNF plays an important role in the benefits of exercise, as it increases the growth of neurons and prolongs their survival. More neurons lead to a stronger connection between the brain and the body. There is, therefore, scientific evidence that proves the assertions that exercise is an important factor in promoting brain health.

DIET AND THE BRAIN

Our brain and our diets are intricately connected, and our diet can directly impact our brain health. This correlation is referred to as the brain-gut connection. I have previously referred to brain "superfoods" in my discussion; this suggests that some foods can promote cognitive function. Our gut has an enteric nervous system, or ENS, a collection of neurons that play a role in digestive functions. The ENS can be considered a second brain found in your gut. Although the ENS is not capable of thought, it is directly linked with the brain and communicates messages back and forth. For example, scientists and studies have found that irritations in the gastrointestinal system can cause significant mood changes and directly impact the brain. This is because of the connection and communication between the central nervous system, which regulates mood and emotions, and the enteric nervous system. To maintain brain health, you need to develop a long-term, healthy dietary regimen that encourages cognitive development and optimal brain function. A healthy and brain-boosting diet should contain a healthy balance of complex carbohydrates, important fatty acids, amino acids, and important vitamins and minerals.

Carbohydrates supply the body with glucose, more commonly known as sugar, which helps to energize the body. Not all carbohydrates are created equal. Processed carbohydrates can be more detrimental than advantageous when feeding the brain and the body. We are surrounded by processed carbohydrates like white bread and sugars, which only provide energy for a brief period and cause the body to "crash," almost like a sugar high. Rather, complex carbohydrates are found in wholegrain foods and fibers. These carbohydrates release energy slowly and consistently, thus maintaining energy levels throughout the day and nourishing the body for longer. This helps to maintain brain function consistently rather than providing sporadic bursts of energy and motivation.

Essential fatty acids are found in Omega-3 and Omega-6 fatty acids. Omega-3 fatty acids can be found in flaxseed and fish, while Omega-6 is found most commonly in poultry, eggs, and avocado.

Amino acids are helpful in mood regulation and thus prevent moodiness and irritability. Milk and oats, for example, contain amino acids that release serotonin, which reduces anxiety and improves sleep. Amino acids also help break down food, provide energy, boost the immune system, build healthy muscle, and maintain healthy digestion. The brain diet and the Mediterranean diet are two main diets that are widely considered brain-healthy diets. I will elaborate more on the foods conducive to brain health and how food can impact our health later in this book.

SOCIALIZATION AND THE BRAIN

Social relationships are an intricate part of our lives. They determine our identity and form an integral part of our development. Establishing and maintaining social connections is very important to maintaining a healthy brain. In the first chapter, I have touched on the connection between empathy and gray matter in the brain. A greater level of socialization has been linked to increased gray matter in the brain, which assists in preventing diseases such as dementia. Socialization provides significant exercise for the brain, as it involves reading facial cues, interpreting language while considering tone, and making several decisions. It is also widely known that isolation and a lack of social interaction can lead to feelings of loneliness and even depression. These are detrimental to the brain, impairing our ability to make responsible decisions. On a less scientific note, interacting with others and listening to the people in our lives can also provide an important change in perspective. It encourages us to focus less on our problems and develop an awareness of those around us. Focusing less on the problems in our lives makes us less likely to suffer from depression and feelings of hopelessness.

THE BRAIN AS AN INSTRUMENT

Have you ever wondered how some people could just drive to different places without using a map or some form of navigation? Or how do cab drivers seem to have an entire city memorized? You may remember my allusion to the brain being like a muscle. The more we use our brains, the more it develops and the more adept it becomes at certain tasks. So, in addition to using our brains as effectively as possible, we need to look after them. This chapter has discussed many ways to ensure our brains are healthy. Sleep, exercise, diet, and socialization determine how well our brains can function.

Furthermore, we need to maintain a healthy lifestyle and avoid habits and substances that can affect our health. We should also be aware of environmental factors that can affect brain development. Neurotoxins like lead, mercury, and pesticides are bountiful, and we must know their effects. We need to shy away from substances that impair cognitive function, such as alcohol and drugs, and even certain medications. We must know what we expose our bodies and brains to and do our best to maintain our physical and mental health. One of the things that we need to work on, especially in today's demanding society, is managing stress.

4

STRESS AND THE BRAIN

In her article on stress, Ruth Kao Barr (2019) says, "Being aware of stress and its harmful effects doesn't mean you need to hold back on living a full life."

Managing stress and its effects on our lives does not mean we must always avoid all stressors. It does not require us to stay away from stressful situations entirely. Rather, being mindful of stress and managing its effects involves being aware of the factors that cause stress and learning how to successfully manage the symptoms. Being mindful of stress and managing it requires us to know where it comes from, what it is, how the brain reacts to it, and how to maintain or deal with it healthily.

CAUSES OF STRESS

Many things in life can cause stress, and this will be different for each person, based on their brains and experiences. We may not all experience the same factors as stress, and we may not all react the same way. There are, however, a few general factors that can cause stress:

- Feeling under pressure from deadlines.
- Experiencing big life changes.
- Feeling a lack of control over a situation.
- Feeling overwhelmed by responsibilities or situations.
- Experiencing discrimination, hatred, or abuse.
- Uncertainty.
- Feeling dissatisfied with life or work.
- Emotional problems.
- Experiencing a traumatic event.
- Having unrealistic expectations.
- Having a lack of access to resources.
- Experiencing conflict with family, friends, or peers.

This list is limited and by no means exhaustive, but it provides an overview of the categories that may be interpreted or experienced as stressful. Stress is often affected by how comfortable or uncomfortable you may feel in a given situation, other life events or changes you may be experiencing at the time, past experiences, self-perception, available resources, or having a lack of resources, and the amount of support that is available to you.

TYPES OF STRESS

Not all stress is bad. Stress is a naturally occurring phenomenon that can help us to get out of dangerous situations or help us to deal with new challenges. However, some stress can harm our health and must be dealt with before they become detrimental. There are different types of stress based on the situation, intensity, and duration of the stress you are experiencing. Depending on the stress category, their symptoms differ, and you may have to address your stress differently.

Acute Stress

This common form of stress occurs when someone experiences or witnesses a disturbing event. These events can include a car accident, losing a loved one, being attacked or witnessing an attack, or being diagnosed with a chronic illness. Some events that cause acute stress are not as intensive or traumatic, such as having a job interview, speaking in front of a crowd, or going to the doctor. Major life events or changes, such as getting married or moving into a new home, can also cause this kind of stress.

Acute stress often does not last long and, therefore, usually does not have any real long-term effects on your health. However, suppose it is not dealt with properly. In that case, acute stress can develop into a more long-term acute stress disorder, lasting anywhere between a few days and a month.

In some cases, stressful events may even lead to the development of Post-Traumatic Stress Disorder, or PTSD, which can significantly impact your health. Acute stress can sometimes cause the same symptoms as PTSD but should not last more than a month. However, if these symptoms persist, it may be necessary to consult a medical professional for professional help.

The symptoms of acute stress can include:

- Increased heart rate and rapid breathing.
- Increased sweating.
- Feeling more irritable.
- Loss of memory of the event.
- Avoiding anyone or anything that reminds you of the event.
- Hyperarousal, which can cause you to start easily.
- Feeling numb and detached.
- Having distressing thoughts, dreams, or flashbacks.
- Insomnia or difficulty sleeping.
- Restlessness.
- Having difficulty focusing.
- Feeling tense.

If you are experiencing these symptoms, dealing with your stress before it becomes a long-term stress disorder is important. The long-term effects can be detrimental if these symptoms are not properly addressed. Talk therapy is one of the most effective ways to deal with common forms of stress. Consulting a therapist or even talking to a friend or family member can help you to work through the traumatic event and consolidate your experience to move past the trauma of the event. However, if this does not provide relief, it may be necessary to consult a doctor for a referral. This may result in medication being prescribed, or your doctor may refer you to a psychologist or psychiatrist. Other forms of therapy, such as cognitive-behavioral therapy, have proven useful in treating this form of stress. Practicing mindfulness or meditation may also be helpful, but seek help if these methods prove ineffective.

Episodic Acute Stress

This form of stress occurs when a person experiences frequent episodes of stress that arise when stressful situations happen consistently. It may also happen when you live in an environment with consistent stressors or are frequently worried about the future. This may include regular doctor's visits, frequent presentations, or a series of meetings you may consider as stressful or worrisome. This often happens with people who are naturally anxious or irritable, who interpret minor stressors as something far worse. This persistent form of stress can lead to a prolonged fight-or-flight response, which can significantly affect the body.

Symptoms of this kind of stress include, but are not limited to:

- Irritability and anger.
- Increased heart rate.
- Panic attacks.
- Indigestion and heartburn.
- Muscle stiffness or muscle pain.

- Heart disease.
- High blood pressure.
- Recurring headaches.

In this case, it may be helpful to consult your doctor. They may refer you to a therapist or prescribe anti-anxiety medication to help with the stress. Alternatively, you may try calming exercises such as meditation and yoga or cognitive-behavioral therapy to better help you deal with these stressors in the future.

Chronic Stress

This is a long-term, consistent stress that offers no relief. This kind of stress is often common in people who deal with long-term, persistent issues such as chronic health or disability or having to take care of someone with these issues. It can also be found in people who experience persistent trauma or stress, such as abuse, a lengthy divorce, financial difficulties, discrimination, or low self-esteem. In addition, it may affect people who face multiple stressors constantly, have little to no support structure, or are prone to negative or catastrophic thinking. Thus, the stressor does not have to be a physical element but can relate to anticipation. This constant stimulation of stress hormones can have catastrophic long-term effects and impede daily functioning.

Symptoms of chronic stress can include the following:

- High blood pressure.
- Anxiety and anxiety disorders.
- A compromised immune system.

- Fatigue and insomnia.
- Persistent headaches.
- Increased risk of heart attacks and cardiovascular disease.
- Depression and low self-esteem.
- Irritability.
- Weight gain (often due to stress eating).
- Digestive issues and nausea.
- Lowered libido and decreased fertility.
- Difficulty coping with daily tasks and responsibilities.
- Feelings of helplessness and hopelessness.

To effectively deal with chronic stress, it is important to identify the source of the stress so that you can deal with the core of the issue. If the issue can be addressed, like changing jobs or moving to a new neighborhood, then these issues must be addressed. However, if the issue cannot be solved, it is necessary to work on developing coping mechanisms. These coping mechanisms can include breathing exercises, mindfulness, meditation, journaling, learning to set boundaries and say no when necessary, developing a healthy diet, getting enough sleep, practicing gratitude, fostering friendships and building a supportive community, yoga, journaling, or exercising. Alternatively, you may seek help from a therapist or psychiatrist to help you develop coping strategies.

HOW DOES STRESS AFFECT THE BRAIN?

Stress is a natural response that protects us from threats and forces the body to react. Stress sends the body into a fight-

or-flight response that helps the brain determine whether to fight the threat or run away to protect itself. This stress signal starts in the amygdala, which then communicates with the hippocampus. In the hippocampus, neurons are activated, which send signals to increase heart rate, which circulates blood faster and prepares your body to react faster. It heightens the senses and puts your body in a state of alertness. Stress can therefore be essential to survival in moments of need. It becomes a problem, however, when stress becomes chronic, as the body stays in fight-or-flight mode and is in a constant state of heightened alertness. Therefore, your body constantly feels threatened and at risk of being attacked. This causes your central nervous system to become dysregulated, causing prolonged stress.

Long-term exposure to stress has been shown to shrink the prefrontal cortex, an important element in decision-making. Thus, chronic stress can impair our ability to make decisions, especially in high-pressure or time-sensitive situations. Long-term stress can also cause the hippocampus to shrink, thus leading to impaired memory and emotional regulation. Long-term stress can affect the plasticity of the hippocampus, which leads to a more intense experience of emotions. It also increases the likelihood of self-criticism, consistent worrying, loneliness, and repetitive negative thinking. It can impair self-control and the ability to adapt to new situations. Chronic stress has been linked to depression, PTSD, and anxiety disorders. Long-term stress can, therefore, physically alter the brain's structure and subsequently affect memory and learning ability, decision-making, and emotional regulation. It also increases the risk of developing mental illnesses.

Several strategies can help with stress relief, many of which I have alluded to already. It is important to note that not all strategies will work for everyone, and certain strategies are relevant only to certain scenarios. Suppose you are in a long-term situation where you face consistent financial stress, for example. In that case, breathing exercises may not be beneficial. You may need to try several methods before finding one that works. In the case of acute stress, some stress-relieving methods may include breathing exercises, cognitive reframing, meditation, or progressive muscle relaxation. These are beneficial to relieving short-term stress, thus allowing you to move on. For consistent, chronic stress, these exercises will not be helpful. Thus, some stress-relieving methods you may use in this case are developing and maintaining supportive relationships, maintaining an exercise regimen, listening to music, following a healthy diet, and regular meditation or therapy. In the case of emotional distress, consider listening to music, talking to a friend or therapist, practicing mindfulness, or keeping a journal to write your feelings down. Finally, to combat burnout, take some time to develop a hobby you enjoy, take some time off to regroup, look for the positives of your job and try to find something you enjoy, or find a sense of humor amid your situation.

GOOD STRESS VS. BAD STRESS

As I have mentioned, stress is not always bad, and it can help us make better decisions or react in times of danger. Good stress, also known by professionals as eustress, motivates or encourages us to act during certain times. Therefore, it is helpful to improve our situation. Bad stress, or distress, causes us to worry about things that are out of our control and things that we cannot change. As a result, we spend time worrying and thinking about situations we cannot change. Therefore, this kind of stress is not helpful in changing the situation. There are a few ways in which you can identify whether what you are experiencing is good or bad stress:

- Firstly, ask yourself whether the thing you are stressing about is something you can handle. Do you have the capabilities, resources, or skills to address the problem you are stressing about? If the answer is no, your stress is not productive or helpful, becoming bad stress.
- The second question to ask yourself is whether you have control over the situation. If yes, you can react and solve the problem or address the situation, thus making your stress helpful. If the answer is no, then you can do nothing to change or address the situation, and you are dealing with bad stress.
- The third thing to consider is whether the situation involves a reward. This could be a promotion at work, marrying your partner, or becoming a parent. Stressing over something with an ultimate reward is useful, as the stress motivates us to work toward a goal. On the other hand, stressing over something without reward is not beneficial and should be dealt with.
- Is your stress temporary, or have you experienced it for extended periods? I have already discussed chronic stress in earlier parts of this chapter. If the

stress you are experiencing lingers, it is not beneficial and can harm your health.

Dealing with stress and differentiating between good and bad stress can be difficult. It takes practice and intention to properly address these issues.

STRESS RELIEVING TECHNIQUES

There are a few measures that you can apply to your life to help you better manage your stress. Some of these have been mentioned in earlier parts of the chapter. Therefore, this is not a comprehensive list. Other things can also help to relieve stress. Still, these general guidelines are helpful to most people and have been backed up with research and testimonies.

Exercise

We have discussed the effects of exercise on the brain. Still, exercise can also help to relieve stress and help to maintain healthy stress levels. First, on a logical note, exercising helps you to focus on something other than your stress. Second, it keeps you from sitting and meditating on your problems for long periods. Third, it improves common mental health issues such as depression and anxiety. Finally, it improves your brain function, enabling you to make faster and better decisions.

Follow a Healthy Diet

Feeling stressed can easily send you into a spiral of not wanting to put effort into grocery shopping or cooking. It can leave you feeling tired, demotivated, and even depressed. A healthy diet is essential in stress management as it affects our brain directly (remember the brain-gut connection?). It has been shown that people who consume large amounts of processed foods and refined sugar are more prone to stress, as these foods lack the nutrients that our brain needs to function properly. Therefore, it is especially important when you are dealing with stress to consume healthy and nutritious foods, as it balances out the brain and improves its ability to think and act healthily.

Minimize Your Screen Time

Society has made us dependent on, and even slaves to, our phones, televisions, and computers. We have become so dependent on them that we use them to pay for goods and services. Extended screen time can be severely detrimental to our health, especially our mental health. Not only does too much screen time affect your sleep, but it is also associated with elevated stress levels. Social media presents a false reality that convinces us we lack in various areas of our lives. We look at others on social media and envy their "perfect lives" and achievements. Social media, however, is not real. It has become a platform for people to present an image of who they wish they were, only presenting their happiest and most accomplished moments.

Furthermore, being tied to our screens consistently also means that we are more likely to take the stresses of work with us wherever we go. We can easily check our emails wherever we are, and phone calls come through at any time of the day. We anxiously think of ways to respond to or avoid text messages. This causes tremendous pressure and prevents us from ever truly taking a break. Make a deliberate plan to set aside or switch off your phone during certain parts of the day, and refrain from looking at screens before bed. This may take some practice and getting used to, but it will improve your sleep and help to reduce stress.

Consider Taking Supplements

You will read more on supplements and their possible benefits on the brain in Chapter 9. Taking these supplements can help to reduce or manage your stress in the long term.

Practice Self-Care

You may have heard the well-known expression: "You cannot pour from an empty cup." If we do not take a break and take time to take care of ourselves and our well-being, we leave ourselves exposed to stress, burnout, and mental decline. Set some time aside for yourself where you can focus on practicing self-care. This might involve reading a book, taking a bath, walking, practicing a hobby, practicing mindfulness, stretching, or doing yoga. This should be something you enjoy, that makes you feel relaxed, and does not involve your work or daily responsibilities. You must make time for yourself and your interests. This will help to relieve stress and revitalize you.

Drink Less Caffeine

Coffee may be good for brain health, but it can be detrimental to people who suffer from chronic stress or anxiety. For example, suppose you feel anxious or jittery after consuming caffeine. In that case, you may consider reducing your caffeine consumption to help relieve your stress.

Socialize

I have already mentioned the importance of having a supportive structure. Spending time with friends and family can be beneficial in many ways. Firstly, you may consider voicing your stress to your friends and family. Doing so provides an outlet for the emotions you experience, and your friends may just have some useful advice. If not, feeling loved and supported regardless of your worries can go a long way to reducing the effects of the stress you may be experiencing. Alternatively, spending time with your friends and family, even without discussing your stress, can benefit your mental health. Feeling a sense of support helps us to feel more secure and may even boost our determination. Talking with friends and family can help take our minds off our stresses and problems, thus relieving those worries. You may even change your perception of the problem or leave with renewed determination and enthusiasm.

Set Healthy Boundaries

Saying no and setting healthy boundaries can be difficult for some people, especially those prone to stress. One of the most important keys to managing a stress-free or stress-less life is learning to set boundaries and saying no when necessary. Setting boundaries and learning to say no when necessary means that you will have less on your plate and can complete tasks effectively and under less pressure. It will also lessen your load and help you maintain your responsibilities more effectively. Not being able to say no often leads to an overload of responsibilities and eventually leaves you exposed to burnout. If you feel like you have too much on your plate or do not have time to help a friend or family member, learn to say "no" or "not now." This may lead to some disappointment, but being honest about your commitments and availability will prevent overcommitting and will show your friends and family that you are reliable and will only say yes when you can afford to. Setting healthy boundaries and saying no when necessary to do so takes practice. Still, it will reduce stress and give you a healthier and more satisfactory life.

Avoid Procrastination

Procrastination is a gnarly and severely detrimental habit that leads to demotivation and failure to complete important tasks on time. When we procrastinate, we put more stress and pressure on ourselves to complete tasks in a significantly shorter, even impossible, amount of time than we need to. Prioritization is important, and avoiding procrastination will enable you to be more productive and finish important tasks. The best way to battle procrastination is to list tasks that need to be completed, order them by priority, and then set realistic deadlines for yourself. You may even want to break big tasks down into smaller tasks with their deadlines. This will ensure you stay on track and avoid unnecessary stress and pressure.

Schedule a Yoga Class

Yoga can be meditative and is very stress relieving. Yoga encourages mindfulness and awareness, thus keeping your body in a state of consciousness. Doing so takes your mind off of your worries and problems and thus decreases your stress levels. Yoga helps calm your mind and lowers stress hormones and blood pressure.

Practice Mindfulness

If yoga is not for you, you may consider practicing mindfulness. The effects are similar, but mindfulness does not require the body movements of yoga. Instead, mindfulness encourages us to be aware of our thoughts and be present at the moment. It can take the form of meditation or mindfulness-based cognitive-behavioral therapy. There are countless resources available on mindfulness and cognitive-behavioral therapy that can assist you in this practice.

Human Touch

You may find this one surprising, but a physical touch from a loved one can have calming effects on our brain and nervous system. Feeling the touch of someone you love and care about helps lower cortisol levels and releases oxytocin, lowering stress levels and promoting calmness. Therefore, cuddling with a loved one can help significantly lower your stress levels.

Spend Time Outside

Spending more time outside or in nature has been linked with reduced stress levels and increased feelings of calmness. Spending as little as ten minutes outside daily can profoundly impact your mental health and reduce the amount of stress you may be feeling. Make time to walk, sit in your garden, visit a park, or hike. This will help you to feel less stressed.

Breathe Deeply

Deep breathing exercises force your heart rate to slow down and thus reduce stress levels. Deep breathing exercises have been used as a relaxation technique. They can help restore your body from fight-or-flight mode to its normal state. Deep breathing forces you to focus on your breaths and your body's response to breathing, thus taking your mind off your problems and allowing your body and mind to relax.

Spend Time With Your Pet

 If you do not have a pet, you may consider adopting one, as pets can help to lower stress and loneliness. Cuddling or loving a pet can have the same effects as showing affection to someone you love. It releases oxytocin in your body, which relieves feelings of anxiety and helps you to feel happier and more relaxed. In addition, having a pet offers more life satisfaction and a sense of purpose, preventing you from falling into depression, self-harm, or having a negative self-image.

Stress can harm our brain health and impair our ability to think, respond appropriately, or make responsible decisions. However, by managing and addressing our stress effectively, we can function better physically and mentally. Now that we understand how stress affects the brain, it is also important to understand how our senses can affect cognition and how to differentiate between reality and fiction.

5

YOUR SENSES AND THE BRAIN

In her book, *When Kids Fly: Solutions for Children with Sensory Integration Challenges*, Sally Frier Dietz states: "I believe the only real limits in life are the ones we put on ourselves and/or others...so I say forget the limits and 'go for it.' You may be surprised at what is possible!"

This statement was directed at kids and people who have sensory difficulties. However, before adequately addressing this quotation, we must understand how sensory information affects the brain and alters how we think and feel.

SENSORY INTEGRATION

We know logically that the brain receives input from our various senses and uses this information to react or decide. Still, on a scientific basis, this can be harder to understand.

When we experience things, we rarely use only one of our senses. Hearing, sight, touch, taste, and smell are intricately connected in formulating memories or interpreting experiences. Thus, our brain interprets information based on multi-sensory integration—using information from multiple senses. However, sensory information is not always integrated, as not all sensory stimuli will have the same origin. Thus, senses will only integrate when they originate from the same source. Sensory integration is essential for brain development. It teaches the brain to differentiate between and integrate information to form a more informed deduction. Unfortunately, some people, like those on the autism spectrum, have difficulty understanding and integrating sensory information, which impedes their development. This is where Dietz's quote is aimed.

Sensory integration refers to the process by which the brain receives and interprets information from the senses and determines an appropriate response. Sensory processing involves how we experience the world and comprises eight senses rather than the basic five. These senses include the five basic senses, as well as vestibular, interoception, and proprioception. Vestibular senses involve balance and coordination controlled by the inner ear. Interoception refers to any form of "feeling" that is going on in your body. This can include anything from emotions to blood pressure and blood sugar levels. Finally, proprioception refers to your body's sense of awareness, movement, and spatial presence. Thus, it involves knowing how you move and how your body relates to its spatial surroundings. Sensory integration, however, relies on tactile, vestibular, and proprioceptive systems.

Sensory integration helps our body to determine an appropriate response to our surroundings or situation based on information provided by our senses. In some cases, people can develop sensory integration disorders, affecting how the brain interprets and reacts to sensory stimuli. In these cases, people often overreact to a situation, experience intense clumsiness or poor coordination, or have difficulty developing or learning certain motor skills.

SENSES AND THE BRAIN

You now know how sensory inputs are interpreted, but how do these sensory inputs travel to the brain in the first place? Sensory signals are translated to electrical signals communicated via neurons to the central nervous system. This change takes place in the sensory receptor. These sensory receptors are specifically coded for a certain sensory stimulus, and they only respond to certain types of sensory input. Sensory information encoded in these receptors includes the stimulus type, the stimulation length, where the stimulus is signaled, and the intensity of the stimulus. Thus, senses related to hearing, tasting, seeing, smelling, and feeling each have their respective receptors and processes for interpreting these senses to determine a certain action or output. The process of sensory integration is activated once the information is received.

The interpreted information then leads to perception, which occurs in the brain. Sensory signals travel through the central nervous system and into the brain, which interprets the information, sorts relevant from irrelevant information, and then sends out a signal for action based on its deduction.

Our brain does not take in or retain everything we see, smell, taste, feel or hear. To do so would be ineffective. Our bodies also cannot take in everything we experience, as there is too much information. Thus, only certain pieces of stimuli are taken in and then communicated via neurons. The neurons in our brain are categorized and organized, almost like a map. This allows for better organization in the brain, more neuron capacity, and better connection and communication between neurons. These maps are divided according to sensory information that communicates the stimuli. Due to the limited capacity of our brains, we only retain some of the information we perceive.

TRAINING YOUR BRAIN

Challenging and exercising your brain is always beneficial as it improves your cognition, helps your brain interpret information faster to determine a reaction, and exposes it to several scenarios and stimuli. Brain exercises do not always have to be taxing, but there are three general guidelines for good exercise. Firstly, brain games should be challenging, as they present a new stimulus for the brain that is not repetitive or predictable. Secondly, a brain game should be complex, forcing your brain to work in more than one dimension. It forces your brain to work on more intricate skills, such as problem-solving or critical or creative thinking. Finally, brain games take practice. There is no use in doing an activity once and giving up. When we practice skills and try again when we fail, that is when the brain is trained and challenged. This also teaches perseverance. For memory to fully consolidate, repetition is needed, which is why we practice.

As you can see, the brain is increasingly more complex and intricate than we can think or imagine. There are many more processes than we know about and functions than we can fathom. Each of our senses plays an important role in perception and brain function, but sight is our primary sense.

* * *

If you are enjoying this book, please consider leaving a review.

* * *

6

VISION AND THE BRAIN

In her famous novel *Jane Eyre*, Charlotte Brontë writes: "The soul, fortunately, has an interpreter—often an unconscious but still a faithful interpreter—in the eye."

Many common sayings and quotations are related to the eyes and their significance to life, wisdom, and truth. Our eyes are our primary source of information, and what we see—consciously or unconsciously—informs more of our lives and decisions than we think.

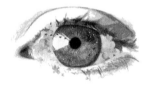

THE IMPORTANCE OF VISION

Out of all eight senses that we possess, sight is the most important of our senses. Out of all our senses, our eyes retain the most information—up to 80 percent of our experience. When our other senses stop working effectively, our eyes compensate for these senses. As a result, our eyes provide more information than we think. For example, when determining how food will taste, our eyes look for rotten spots or mold. In addition, they can often determine flavor based on the color of the food.

Furthermore, when we meet new people, we see the first information available about those people, hence the expression "judging a book by its cover." Much of our world and the information we take in rely on sight. Sight allows us to judge things from afar before encountering them with our other senses. This will often protect us from entering dangerous situations. Imagine yourself walking in the city, for example. Suppose you see that there are many people around you, and they are going about their business normally. In that case, you feel comfortable entering those situations. If, on the other hand, you encounter a dark and isolated alley, you are likely to turn away and proceed somewhere you feel safer. Therefore, although all our senses are important for a more holistic idea of our experiences, sight allows us to prejudge certain people, places, and things and can ultimately ensure our safety.

HOW VISION WORKS

We already know that what we experience with our senses is processed through neurons that send signals between the brain and the body. However, the way that information is received through vision is very complicated.

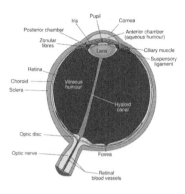

Think of your eyes like a camera. When we look at objects around us, light bounces off the objects and enters the eyes through the cornea, a thin layer on the outside of the eyes. The cornea then helps to direct this light source to the pupil and the iris, which work together to regulate the amount of light that enters the eye and thus protect it from damage. The iris is the part that is colored, thus showing your eye color. The pupil is the black circle found in the middle of your eye. Pupils sometimes appear bigger or smaller, and this is because the iris shrinks and grows to control the amount of light that enters the eye. This is very much like a camera lens when you adjust the aperture. The light that enters the pupil then goes through the eye's lens, which focuses on the object and then directs light to the retina in the back of the eye. The retina contains rods and cones to help it process and project visual information. Cones are responsible for helping you see in color, while rods help to translate visual information in lower light. Cones and rods are responsible for processing and translating visual information into electronic information and then sending that information to the brain. Your optic nerve is the messenger that relays and communicates this information to the visual cortex in the back of the brain. Your visual cortex then translates the information into a visual map.

You may have heard that we see images upside down, and our brain rotates images the right way up. Felix Platter developed the theory in the 16th century that our eye works like an optic, and the retina is a receptor. Thus, light that enters the cornea is refracted—it changes direction—and forms an image on the retina, which is then related to the brain. There is one small catch with this process. It implies that we see objects and images upside down. This happens because the retina is curved and therefore causes the image we see to invert itself. Does this mean that what we see is really upside down? Luckily not. The brain takes the information and inverts it back to how it should be, turning it the right side up. Psychologist George Stratton proved the brain's power in the 1980s when he wore glasses that inverted everything he saw—turning it upside down. Within four days, however, his brain had unraveled the visual information. It reverted it to the way it should be—right side up. Thus, our brain does more than simply interpret visual information and project images.

To form a three-dimensional image, the brain combines or overlays the two two-dimensional images from each retina to form one cohesive image, thus giving us better depth perception. Our minds are, therefore, powerful and extremely advanced. There are innumerable processes taking place every second for us to be able to see and interpret visual information, and thousands more processes take place for the body to function effectively.

BODY LANGUAGE AND FACIAL EXPRESSIONS—
IT'S ALL IN THE EYES

You may have heard the expression: "The eyes are the window to the soul." This may or may not have been written as a symbolic statement, but it has some truth. There is a reason why we tend to avert our eyes when we feel uncomfortable or are fibbing. When we feel discouraged, we tend to avoid people's eyes and rather look down. There is an element of emotion that is seen in the eyes. Looking deeply enough, you can see if someone feels uncomfortable, sad, angry, or happy—all by looking into their eyes. There is some physiological explanation for this phenomenon. People who experience emotions relating to discrimination, such as disgust and suspicion, generally narrow their eyes, as they tend to be more focused and determined.

On the other hand, people who experience sensitive emotions, such as fear or awe, tend to have bigger, more open eyes. This is because our emotions are intricately connected with the eyes, affecting the size of our eyes, pupil movement, and eyebrow movement. Fortunately for us, reading others' facial expressions and body language can help us perceive and understand the world around us.

Facial expressions are a great way to communicate a message. However, they quickly give away your true feelings if your words do not align with what you feel or want to say. Facial expressions help us interpret what someone means. Still, it helps us to determine whether they are lying and, therefore, whether we can trust them. Facial expressions can help us understand what other people are feeling. Still, there are general interpretations that are not narrowed down to a specific emotion. This is because there are countless different and complex emotions that we feel. Facial expressions can narrow these down to the most basic ones, such as fear, happiness, sadness, anger, surprise, disgust, and distress. Some facial expressions last only a moment before instinct kicks in, and we try to hide our emotions as an act of self-preservation. These are called micro-expressions and can tell much about a person's feelings. Identifying microexpressions can be very tricky, as they are fleeting and momentary. When considering someone's facial expressions, we must look at their eyes, eyebrows, and mouth.

A person's eyes can also tell a lot about what they are thinking or feeling, and there are different parts of the eye that we need to look at when we are looking for these answers. People's gaze can provide a lot of information about their interests, feelings, and the truth of what they are saying. For instance, someone who looks directly into your eyes when you are talking is interested and listens intently to what you are saying. However, if they frequently look away, it may indicate they are distracted or not paying attention to your conversation. If the person who is speaking breaks eye contact frequently, it may indicate discomfort or even dishonesty. People trying to hide their true feelings also tend to look away often. You can also gain much information about a person's disposition if they are blinking abnormally. A person who blinks too much is most likely distressed or uncomfortable.

On the other hand, someone who blinks abnormally little might be trying to control their movements deliberately, indicating that they are hiding something. Pupil dilation is also very informative, especially since it cannot be controlled by sheer will. Eyes that are highly dilated, for example, indicate interest or arousal. The eyes can therefore give away much information about the person you are talking to.

The eyebrows are connected to eye movement and can often give away much of what a person is feeling, even for a moment. Raised or arched eyebrows indicate surprise, showing that someone was caught off guard or did not expect you to say what you did. If the eyebrows are close together and lowered, this can indicate anger, sadness, or fear. It may also indicate intense concentration, depending on the circumstances. Finally, suppose the eyebrows are raised slightly and drawn together in the inner corners. In that case, that may indicate intense sadness or concern. These can be hard to identify by looking at the eyebrows alone. When interpreting expressions based on eyebrow movement, it is important that you consider context and look at the eyes and mouth to narrow down your interpretation.

The mouth is another part of facial expressions that can be very informative. This can be tricky, however, as people often use their mouths as one of the first and main ways to control their facial expressions. For example, a smiling person might be experiencing happiness or showing cynicism or sarcasm. That person may also be forcing a smile to reassure the people around them and hide their true feelings. Pursed or tight lips often allude to feelings of distrust or disapproval. Thus, when a person purses their lips, you know that they do not approve in one way or another. Lip biting usually indicates stress or worry, but certain situations may also indicate arousal. People who cover their mouths are more than likely trying to hide a reaction or emotion, such as smirking or smiling. A very simple indicator of a person's overall condition is to look at the corners of their mouth. A person experiencing a positive emotion such as happiness or optimism will have the corners of their mouth pointing slightly upward. In contrast, someone with negative emotions or pessimism will have the corners of their mouth turned down.

Body language constitutes between 60 and 65 percent of our communication. Therefore, our eyes are essential in helping us understand what people are trying to convey or communicate. This communication lies in the eyes and overall facial expressions, gestures, posture, and body movement. Understanding body language is important because, although a person may say one thing, they can, and often do, mean something completely different from what they communicate verbally. This can be determined and interpreted through body language and facial expressions.

Positioning someone's arms and legs can be informative and give away their true feelings easily. If a person's body language is closed off, it implies distrust or unhappiness with the situation. Open body language, on the other hand, indicates trust and comfortability. Crossed arms can be interpreted as being defensive or trying to protect oneself. It can show insecurity and an attempt to distract oneself from the situation or the other person. Although crossed arms are often associated with anger, it is more common in people with self-defensive tendencies. Depending on the situation, people who place their hands on their hips are generally either showing control or aggression. Crossed legs, like crossed arms, are also self-defense mechanisms that show the desire to close oneself off or protect oneself. Fidgeting or tapping can indicate boredom, frustration, impatience, or nervousness.

Our eyes are, therefore, essential for our survival. They see and interpret the world around us and warn us of immediate dangers. They help us determine where it may or may not be safe to go and which foods may or may not be safe to eat, and they can also help to interpret the non-verbal aspects of our communication with others. Although our eyes are not always trustworthy, they are our first point of interaction with the people and places around us. Our vision is an important part of how we see and interpret the world. Reading and interpreting body language can be very beneficial for our communication skills and help us develop and maintain supportive relationships. The best way to improve this skill is through practice.

7

SOCIALIZATION AND THE BRAIN

"I remind myself every morning: Nothing I say this day will teach me anything. So if I'm going to learn, I must do it by listening."

— LARRY KING

Many of us, when we think of socialization, think of talking. Although talking is an important part of social interaction, it is neither the only nor the most important aspect. Many people overlook listening as social interaction. Listening is as important, if not more important, than talking in a relationship. It is through listening that we get to know the people around us. It is how we unpack their experiences and personalities and how we form connections. Only by listening can we identify common denominators and aspects by which we can connect with those around us. I have discussed earlier in my book why socialization is so important to brain development. Here, we will delve deeper into the role of socialization in our development and the functioning and development of the brain.

THE IMPORTANCE OF COMMUNICATION

Socialization is an integral part of human existence. Communication with the people around us is the only way to effectively socialize. Logically, communication allows us to interact with people around us and convey and receive messages essential to our survival and development as a species. Modern society is filled with gadgets and developments that result from a desire to communicate faster and more effectively. From the development of writing and printing to more innovations like telephones and email, the human species has shown a growing and ever-evolving desire to connect and communicate with others around us.

We have seen in earlier chapters how communication and socialization with others can benefit brain health and development. Still, there is a flip side to this coin. A lack of socialization and communication can harm development and cognitive functioning. Lack of socialization during childhood can be especially detrimental, as this will inhibit the development of certain important skills and abilities. For example, a lack of communication during childhood can impede these abilities and affect language learning abilities for the rest of their life. Furthermore, children not exposed to socialization during their early years may struggle with socialization for the rest of their lives. This happens because, during the developmental phase, the brain does not develop these important foundations and is unable to respond appropriately.

Socialization encourages and improves the effective functioning of the brain, as it presents the brain with a consistent stream of complicated scenarios, forcing it to analyze, interpret, and react continually. This may explain why socializing can be such a taxing activity for some. Although socialization can be intimidating or taxing for some people, it is important to expose yourself to social situations to help your brain develop and to provide stimulation. Not all socialization needs to be unpleasant, and there are ways to make it more enjoyable. Having coffee with a friend, organizing a family gathering, or joining a club can all be beneficial.

HOW DOES COMMUNICATION WORK?

Communication seems simple yet intricate and complicated —especially when you consider its importance in brain development and health. It becomes even more intricate and complicated when we consider the different communication styles that we all possess. These different communication styles can make communication significantly more challenging, not to mention all the mental differences and mood-related issues we all have. Then we also need to consider cultural, religious, racial, and gender differences. The complications are countless. So how does communication then work, and how does it affect our brains? Communication involves various parts of the brain for various functions. Since it involves speaking, it engages most parts of the brain, making it so challenging and rewarding. Since communication involves various parts of the brain, our brain also influences how we communicate and determines our communication style. Before we can delve deeper into the science behind communication, there are five main communication styles to consider.

- Social communicators flourish in social situations. They are comfortable in a social setting and can communicate well with others. They also tend to be skilled at interpreting social cues, facial expressions, and body language.
- Contextual communicators, despite the name, are not adept at adjusting their communication style to the context. Rather, they tell the truth plainly and tend to be very forward. However, these people may be seen as socially unacceptable in some contexts as they tend to lack tact and may be seen by some as too forceful.
- Linguistic communicators communicate best by the words they choose to use. They are often very literal and descriptive when they speak. They usually have a very good vocabulary and are often readers and sometimes writers. These people may have difficulty picking up on figures of speech and figurative language. They are also most likely to correct your grammatical errors in a conversation.

- Visual communicators are adept at creating mental pictures. They can describe what they see in intricate detail and are often good at or interested in visual arts.
- Cerebral communicators are deep thinkers. They are often very quiet, and you may find that when they do speak, their words are meaningful and profound. These people tend to think carefully before they say anything and only speak when they feel it is necessary.

Communicating can be challenging when we do not understand each other's communication type. But practicing is the only way to develop differentiation and the skill to communicate with different people. In addition, due to neuroplasticity, your brain can learn to respond and communicate better with people of different communication styles. Therefore, the more you practice, the more adept you will become at communication.

When we listen to people talking and sharing stories, our brain goes through what is known as neural entrainment. This happens when brain waves and responses synchronize with the sounds produced by a speaker. Uri Hasson (2017) conducted several experiments to determine how the brain responds to communication. His studies found that when the listener shows an understanding of the speaker's story, the speaker and the listener have similar brain activity and brain waves on an MRI scan. Therefore, when we communicate effectively and can understand each other's communication, we form a mental image, and similar experiences occur in the brain, indicating comprehension. On the other hand, when miscommunication occurs, or one of the participants knows that the other does not, the mental picture and brain activity will differ, thus leading to a lapse in the communication process. This indicates that the communication process proves ineffective when the speaker and listener do not have common ground.

This is where compassion becomes important, which is why listening is an integral part of communication. When lapses in communication occur, it is important to ask questions to ascertain which fragment of information you may be missing or to inform the other person of the information they may be lacking. This is where the communication gap can be filled and understanding once again achieved. This experiment indicates why communication can often result in differences and conflict, especially when one or both parties believe they have all the information.

SOCIALIZATION—WHAT IS IT AND WHY IS IT SO IMPORTANT?

Socialization is one of the things that sets human beings apart from other species of animals. Whereas other animals communicate as a means of survival, humans communicate to establish connections and possess the ability to sympathize with those around us. Socializing and establishing relationships with the people around us is classified as one of our basic human needs. Socialization involves knowledge and understanding of social norms and customs. What makes socialization so complex is that it is often context-dependent. Specific methods of communication may be acceptable in one context but not another, or it may mean different things depending on where you are or who you speak to.

There are two stages in which socialization mainly takes place. The first stage, primary socialization, happens between birth and adolescence, while secondary socialization takes place during adulthood. Primary socialization lays the foundation for communication and interaction with others. When we learn what is and is not acceptable, we know how to communicate with others using the various media available to us. Secondary socialization occurs when people find themselves in new environments and situations and are forced to learn and interpret new social customs and laws. This form of socialization continues throughout life, as communication and societies are ever-evolving, and social customs and norms are constantly changing. Socialization is an integral part of becoming part of a group or community. It serves as a form of control, establishing a set of customs and laws people must abide by. Socialization has many uses and purposes—establishing coherent communication, encouraging certain behaviors while discouraging others, and preparing people to take on a particular role in society.

Socialization is not merely about communicating. It involves relationships and communication but is also primarily concerned with social structure. Three main parts or aspects of socialization need to be considered. The first aspect is context. This broad concept includes race, culture, gender, history, and language and considers people's position within these areas. Context can influence socialization in several ways. The context in which a person grows up can tremendously impact their socialization. Each social and socio-economic environment has values and attributes they deem worthy and necessary. Thus, people from different social and socio-economic backgrounds will have grown up emphasizing different values. Context also involves issues surrounding gender and race, which can significantly impact your worldview. Gender inequality and stereotypes are a norm in certain societies, and people who grow up in these societies will learn to perpetuate these roles and stereotypes. The same goes for the issue of race. Some communities and families tend to be more racist or racially aware than others. They will inflict these ideas on their children. These aspects will undeniably affect how you interact with the people around you. Content and process are the second aspects of socialization. This relates to each family's systems and processes. In some families, for example, children are expected to do chores regularly.

In contrast, other children may never be required to work around the house. Schooling is another example of content and process, as learners must adhere to specific rules and follow a code of conduct. This may also differ based on the area and school in which a child is placed. Not all elements of content and process are written or officially intended. Some of these may be reinforced through expectations and unspoken rules. It includes what is deemed acceptable or unacceptable by a family or schooling environment. Finally, results are the final stage of socialization. This is the outcome of socialization—how a person thinks and acts after these two processes have occurred.

As you can imagine, there are also different forms of socialization that take place. Group socialization occurs when a person is influenced by groups of people, such as their peers. These groups will influence how they think and act, dress, and even their goals and aspirations. Organizational socialization happens within an organization or institution when a person is expected to adhere to certain rules and norms. Each organization and workplace has its own rules and code of conduct. They may even have different dress codes or work demands. Therefore, each time a person enters a new workplace or organization, they need to learn these rules and expectations to adhere to the social environment of that institution or organization. Anticipatory socialization occurs when a person prepares for a new role, job, or phase of their life. It involves anticipating the social norms and conduct and what may be expected of them in this role. They may seek advice from someone with more experience or undergo training to prepare them for their new role or position. Finally, forced socialization occurs in institutions such as prisons, military units, mental institutions, or boarding schools. This form of socialization is generally aimed at people deemed unfit for society due to not adhering to social norms or rules. These people are forcefully re-socialized to ensure that they comply with social expectations and behave in a socially acceptable manner. This form of socialization may range from mere rehabilitation to enforcing an entirely new identity for the person in question.

Socialization plays an integral part in maintaining some form of social coherence and introducing people into the social world. Without it, communication would be tremendously challenging, if not impossible. Socialization brings some control and standard into communicating and interacting with the people around us. It teaches our brain how to think and respond in certain situations and helps construct a more harmonious society. Ultimately, socialization helps us form more meaningful connections, which is essential in establishing a supportive community and improving our brain health. There are many other things that can also help to improve and maintain brain health and development, one of which is keeping an active and stimulated mind.

8

EXERCISING THE BRAIN

We have examined how the brain is like a muscle that can be trained and enhanced. Keeping our brains sharp and exercising is the key to shaping and developing our brains to function faster and more effectively. Through training, we can improve memory, speed up our brain reaction time, and learn to make better and faster decisions over time. There are various factors to consider when we examine our brain's ability and training. Our emotions, environment, and level of development can all affect how we think and act and can influence how we process information. We need to acknowledge that just as all brains are uniquely wired and developed, all brains also have a unique ability to adapt. If the brain is trained and your training focuses on the right areas, you can rewire it and teach it to think and react differently or more effectively.

THE BRAIN AS A MUSCLE

We have established that the number of neurons in the brain is by no means fixed, and the brain can produce more neurons. The more we exercise the brain, the more neurons are created and the stronger the connections between these neurons, thus improving our cognitive abilities. There is a link between physical exercise and brain exercise. This is because physical activity releases proteins like cathepsin b, which promotes brain development and adaptation. Physical training not only involves physical muscles, but it involves our brain muscles and develops essential qualities such as perseverance and grit. These can make us more adept at mental challenges, as we are unwilling to give up.

Furthermore, your brain also needs to keep up with the physical changes accompanying exercise. Thus, you are also training your brain and teaching it to adapt. As with many things, practice is the key to perfecting a skill. Thus, if we practice playing the piano to become better pianists and target specific muscles to master certain exercises, why do we not apply the same principles to the brain? If we aim to improve our memory, we need to engage in more activities requiring us to form and recall memories. We must present ourselves with increasingly challenging tasks to become more adept at critical thinking. Therefore, to become better thinkers and improve our brain's abilities, we need to exercise our brain regularly.

BENEFITS OF BRAIN TRAINING

Training our brains has many obvious benefits, some of which are better brain function and a sharper mind. One of the main benefits of brain training is improved memory. Since training involves the brain learning and remembering new things consistently, it will strengthen your formation and recall of information, thus enabling you to remember things more easily. Brain training can also come with specific desirable behavioral changes. Certain behaviors, like a tendency to get distracted or procrastinate, may change if you train your brain effectively. It can enhance focus and determination and even improve your mood. Brain training will undoubtedly increase your focus and lengthen your attention span, allowing you to work more productively for more extended periods. This can be highly beneficial, as it will take many of the stresses associated with procrastination and a hefty workload off your shoulders. Exercising your brain will also help you to reduce your reaction time, enabling your brain to come to conclusions faster and make decisions more quickly without jeopardizing your judgment. Brain training will also allow you to plan more effectively, preparing you for what is to come and reducing the stress and pressure of future events. This enables you to have a goal-oriented approach where your decisions and steps focus on achieving a desired goal or outcome. Training your brain can have countless benefits, and it has no downside.

Many people believe that the brain declines after a certain number of years. Although this may be true to some extent, it is by no means inevitable. Keeping an active brain can slow down cognitive decline and even improve cognitive function after the brain has started declining. For example, if you are noticing lapses in your memory, that does not mean it is too late for you. Exercising your brain can help counteract the effects of brain aging. Thanks to neuroplasticity, there is always time to train your brain and improve your thinking. It is, therefore, beneficial to improving mental function and slowing or preventing cognitive decline, and keeping you sharp and healthy throughout your life.

PHYSICAL EXERCISE FOR BRAIN TRAINING

Chapter two covers mental exercises and activities that can be done to improve brain health, but what about physical activities? We have established that physical exercise is linked to brain exercises, and specific exercises can be more beneficial for brain health than others. For example, although deadlifts and heavy weights are conducive to making you look better physically, cardiovascular exercises are more conducive to improved brain health. These are some of the most accessible kinds of activities and are an easy challenge to start.

Firstly, consider going for a walk regularly. Thirty minutes every day can help stimulate the brain and improve your cognitive functioning and physical health. Walking improves blood flow throughout the body, which helps the brain to function better and faster. Rowing is another exercise you might consider, as it improves blood flow. Rowing can boost your self-confidence and self-esteem very quickly, which is beneficial to your mental and physical health. Swimming is an exercise that you may enjoy on a hot day while boosting your brain. Swimming has been shown to release BDNF, which protects and produces brain cells, strengthening the connection between your brain and the rest of your body. It will also help to regulate your mood, improve blood circulation, and help you sleep better. Yoga can be physically and mentally beneficial, encouraging mindfulness and deep breathing techniques. Yoga is excellent for mastering your body and toning your muscles. Still, it also reduces stress and promotes awareness of our bodies. Strength training may not be as aerobic as the other exercises mentioned here. Still, there is a link between strength training and brain training. Strength training can help to regulate your mood and improve cognitive functioning. In addition, it has been shown to reduce brain degeneration. The best strength training exercises are the ones that focus on multiple muscles at once, as this burns more calories and proves to be more effective.

You may not be an athlete, but exercise, however intense, can help you to improve your cognitive function. Start at a beginner level and build up from there.  Remember that exercise has numerous benefits for various aspects of our lives and bodies, which is another reason to begin exercising. It does not have to be done at a professional level, and it does not have to be taxing. Incorporate music into your exercises to make them more relaxing and doable. You will surely reap the long-term benefits if you start.

MEDITATION FOR BRAIN TRAINING

It is not only physical exercise that is good for brain health and training. Meditation can also be very beneficial and improve cognitive health and ability. Meditation, as discussed in earlier parts of this book, helps to improve mindfulness and reduce stress and anxiety, thus relieving their effects on the brain. We have gone over the impact of stress on the mind and body, and you know that stress can harm your brain.

There are various types of meditations, each with its techniques and benefits. They may not all suit your style or personality, so you should try different methods to see which suits you best. Concentration meditation is centered around focusing your mind. Heart-centered meditation requires a quieting of the mind and then concentrating on the heart—one of the body's energy centers. Mindfulness meditation focuses objectively on negative thoughts and encourages you to experience them and let them pass through your body and mind without affecting you negatively. The ultimate goal here is to achieve calmness and peace amid negativity. Tai chi and qigong are more physical forms of exercise that involve bodily movements combined with breathing and focus on achieving peace. Transcendental meditation consists of the repetition of a mantra to help quieten your mind and achieve a state of awareness. Finally, walking meditation is also a physical form that requires a combined focus of body and mind to help you align your breathing with your footsteps, believed to bring harmony between the body and mind.

Meditation can be done individually or as part of a group. Practicing meditation will help you calm your mind and body, thus allowing you to think more clearly and counteracting the effects of stress on the mind and body.

Tai Chi

Tai chi has many proven benefits for both physical and brain health. Physically, tai chi can improve flexibility, balance, and strength while reducing stress and anxiety through breathing and focus. Tai Chi has been linked to lowered joint pain from osteoarthritis and is also associated with lowered blood pressure and improved autonomic nervous system regulation. The movements and focus required in practicing tai chi have even been linked to reduced dizziness and vertigo in people who have previously experienced these. In addition, tai chi practice can help improve focus, concentration, memory, and motor skills. It helps to strengthen neurons in the brain and can even improve muscle recovery time. This is, therefore, a beneficial practice for several reasons. It can benefit your physical and brain health and improve your physical and mental performance.

Yoga

We have already discussed some of the benefits of practicing yoga, including reducing stress and anxiety and regulating blood pressure. Yoga has been widely accepted as a meditative and calming practice. Many have reaped physical benefits, including increased strength and toned muscles. Yoga has been shown to have numerous benefits for the brain as well. A study by Gothe et al. (2019) investigates the effects of yoga on the brain. They found that yoga can affect the physical anatomy of the brain, thus causing physical and structural changes in the brain. In this study, yoga was found to have improved memory and learning, reduced risk of neurodegenerative diseases and chronic stress, better coordination, and better emotional regulation. Yoga is beneficial to physical and brain health in many areas and can improve your cognition. The nature of yoga also indicates that it improves focus and concentration, as it requires a simultaneous awareness of breathing techniques and body movements.

Heliotherapy

Heliotherapy refers simply to the use of sunlight for medicinal or therapeutic purposes. Thus, when I say heliotherapy, I mean getting more exposure to sunlight. Sunlight is a natural source of vitamin D, which is good for bone strength and helps to strengthen the immune system. Exposure to sunlight can also have several other benefits, such as healthier and clearer skin. In ancient civilizations, sunlight was considered a natural healing remedy and was said to have many health benefits. For example, sunbathing has been linked to reduced blood sugar, improved blood sugar regulation, healthier cholesterol levels, and even higher immunity. Heliotherapy has also proved beneficial for people who suffer from psychological disorders such as depression and bipolar disorder because it releases endorphins which are associated with feelings of happiness and overall improved mood.

There are many warnings about the harmful effects of spending too much time in the sun due to the radiation it releases. This does not mean we should discard all of the benefits sunlight offers and stay inside as often as possible. There are some things you can do to protect yourself against the harmful effects of the sun while still benefiting from its positive effects. Firstly, you can protect your internal body from the effects of ultraviolet rays by including fatty fish in your diet. Green tea can also have the same effect. Getting enough sleep can help your skin repair and rejuvenate itself and strengthen your immune system to protect you from damage. Midday is the best time for sunbathing, as this is when ultraviolet rays are at their weakest, exposing you to minimal radiation. If you know you will be in direct sunlight for over 20 minutes, apply sunscreen to protect your skin against harmful ultraviolet rays. Suppose you have a skin condition that makes you sensitive to light, or you are taking chronic medication. In that case, you should consult your doctor before considering heliotherapy. Following these tips will help you to benefit from heliotherapy while suffering minimal damage.

Nature and Animal Therapy

Have you ever felt refreshed or revitalized in a naturally beautiful place? Or have you ever felt burnt out and just needed to spend time in nature? Nature has many natural healing effects. Nature therapy or ecotherapy is based on the idea that spending time in nature can have healing effects. Many ancient civilizations believed in the same thing and were concerned with caring for the environment and nurturing their natural resources. Spending time in nature can have many benefits, including brain stimulation and improved cognition. It offers a break from the busyness of life and helps us to destress and calm our minds. It distracts from the demands and pressures of our everyday lives, thus giving the brain a chance to rest. Ecotherapy can take many forms, some as simple as meditating in a natural environment. Some other examples are gardening, exercising outside, and engaging in adventurous outdoor activities such as river rafting or rock climbing.

Spending time with animals has also been shown to reduce stress and loneliness. Petting an animal can release hormones that make you less stressed and improve your mood. Animal therapy has been used as a form of therapy, along with other treatments, to help people with mental and physical disabilities. The nature of the therapy differs based on the person's needs and the desired outcome. Still, it ranges from helping to reduce pain by providing comfort, increasing motivation levels, improving motor skills, or developing certain social skills. Animal therapy can improve mental health by reducing stress and anxiety, lowering pain levels and even perceptions of pain, decreasing loneliness, increasing a sense of support and understanding, and increasing motivation. Animal therapy has even improved physical conditions such as epilepsy, heart failure, and recovery from certain injuries or medical conditions. Nature and animal therapy can therefore benefit your physical, mental, and brain health and help reduce stress and improve overall coping mechanisms.

Therefore, various forms of exercise and therapy are important and beneficial to physical and brain health. To maintain these benefits, however, it is also essential to maintain a healthy gut through a balanced diet.

9

BRAIN FOOD

Brain health is not unrelated to other areas in our bodies, and health issues in other parts of the body will affect brain health. For example, health complications such as obesity and diabetes have been shown to affect cognition and brain performance. Likewise, an unhealthy diet has been linked to memory impairment or reduction. We have already discussed the tremendous impact that our gut and brain are connected, and it is important to establish and maintain a healthy and nutritious diet. According to studies conducted by Ekstrand et al. (2021), diet can directly impact five areas of our brain—brain development and the growth of neurons, neurotransmitters, cognition and memory, proteostasis, and deterioration caused by chronic inflammation.

BRAIN-BOOSTING FOODS

If your digestive system has such a significant impact on your mental health, it follows that to take care of your brain health, you should also take care of your gut. The best way to do this is through your diet. Certain foods improve brain health and boost performance, including memory and concentration.

Fatty Fish

Fatty fish includes salmon, trout, sardines, herring, and albacore tuna, which are rich in omega-3 fatty acids. Our brains consist of 60 percent fat, half of which are omega-3 fatty acids. These acids are used to build nerve and brain cells needed for memory and learning. Aside from learning abilities, these fatty acids are also known to slow down mental decline and help prevent neurodegenerative diseases like Alzheimer's disease and dementia. Evidence suggests eating more fish is linked to having more gray matter in the brain, thus improving the production of neurons. A lack of omega-3 fatty acids has also been linked to a greater likelihood of developing depression. Thus, eating fatty fish can benefit your brain health and improve cognitive functioning tremendously.

Coffee

Coffee contains caffeine and antioxidants, which are beneficial in supporting brain health. Caffeine can support the brain by increasing alertness and blocking hormones that make you sleepy. It also helps to improve your mood by releasing dopamine and improves concentration. Prolonged coffee consumption is also linked to a reduced risk of neurodegenerative diseases, which may be due to the antioxidants found in coffee.

Blueberries

Blueberries and other dark berries are also very good for brain health. This is because they contain anthocyanins—pigments that have anti-inflammatory and antioxidant effects. Antioxidants help to reduce stress and inflammation and help in preventing neurodegenerative diseases. Furthermore, these berries have also been shown to improve the connections between neurons, thus improving cognitive functions such as memory.

Turmeric

Turmeric is a yellow spice that is often used in curries. It contains curcumin, which can enter directly into the brain and directly affects the brain cells. Turmeric, like berries, also has antioxidants and anti-inflammatory qualities. It has been known to improve memory (and thus also prevent neurodegenerative diseases), ease depression through the release of dopamine and serotonin, and promote the growth of new brain cells, thus increasing brain matter and improving cognition. Although turmeric contains curcumin, the amount of curcumin found in turmeric is very small. Thus, taking curcumin supplements may be more beneficial to truly experience its benefits.

Broccoli

Broccoli also contains antioxidants that are beneficial to your brain's health. For example, it is rich in vitamin K, which promotes blood clotting in case of injury and helps wounds to heal. It also forms sphingolipids, an essential fat in brain cells. In addition, vitamin K helps to improve memory and overall cognitive function.

Pumpkin Seeds

Pumpkin seeds contain antioxidants that protect the body from free-radical stress. Free radicals are unstable atoms that can cause harm to the body by damaging cells, causing illness, or speeding up the aging process. Thus, pumpkin seeds can help to protect the body from these attacks. They also contain zinc, magnesium, copper, and iron, which benefit the body's functioning. Zinc improves nerve signaling, thus improving the connection between nerves and preventing neurodegenerative diseases. Magnesium helps to improve learning and memory and contributes to the prevention of depression, epilepsy, and migraines. Copper also plays an important role in strengthening nerve signals and preventing neurodegenerative diseases. Finally, iron is linked to improved wakefulness and cognitive function.

Dark Chocolate

Yes, dark chocolate is good for your brain. Dark chocolate and cocoa powder contain flavonoids, antioxidants, and caffeine, all brain-boosting elements. I refer specifically to dark chocolate, not all chocolate, as dark chocolate generally contains a 70 percent or higher concentration of cocoa. Flavonoids are beneficial to learning and memory and help to slow down mental decline. Chocolate also releases hormones that improve mood.

Nuts

Nuts are especially important in maintaining heart health, but as we know, heart health is also crucial to brain health. Consuming nuts regularly has been shown to reduce the rate and risk of cognitive decline in old age. It also contributes to improved memory. Nuts contain several healthy and beneficial nutrients to the body and brain, such as antioxidants, Vitamin E, which protects against free-radical damage, and healthy fats. Walnuts are most beneficial, as they also contain omega-3 fatty acids.

Oranges

These are not only helpful in combating the flu but can also help to prevent mental decline. The high dosage of Vitamin C found in oranges is linked to improved memory and focus, a lengthened attention span and faster decision-making. In addition, it protects the body from free-radical damage and the brain from neurodegenerative diseases. Of course, oranges are not the only food that is high in Vitamin C. You can also experience the same benefits from eating kiwis, tomatoes, bell peppers, strawberries, and guavas.

Eggs

Eggs are high in protein, which is good for physical health. It also supports brain health, containing vitamins B12 and B6, choline, and folate. Choline supports the production of acetylcholine, which improves mood and memory. Vitamin B is known to slow down mental decline and reduce the risk of developing depression. Vitamin B12 is also linked to regulating sugar levels, which reduces the risk of insulin resistance and related diseases such as diabetes.

Green Tea

Like coffee, green tea also contains caffeine, which improves mental performance, increases alertness and boosts memory and concentration. It also contains an antioxidant called L-theanine, which promotes relaxation and reduces stress and anxiety. As a result, green tea helps to prevent neurodegenerative diseases and mental decline.

This is not a comprehensive list and provides only some foods considered most beneficial to brain health. Including these foods in your diet will help protect your brain while improving memory and cognition. You are more likely to have better emotional and mood regulation. You will also reap the physical benefits of following a healthy diet.

BRAIN-BOOSTING MACRO AND MICRONUTRIENTS

Macronutrients are the nutrients your body needs to consume to maintain itself. At the same time, micronutrients are required in much smaller amounts. Certain nutrients are essential for brain health and can improve cognition and all associated functions. These nutrients are best consumed naturally through the food that we eat and what we drink. Still, certain micronutrients can be taken as supplements where necessary. Remember that supplements should serve only as a supplementary source of nutrients rather than a replacement for a healthy and balanced diet.

Macronutrients

Our bodies require three main macronutrients to function at their best—protein, fat, and carbohydrates. However, not all of these are equal, and some foods that fall under these categories can do more harm than good. For example, proteins are consumed by the body and broken down into amino acids. These acids are one of the main components of neurotransmitters in the brain. These neurotransmitters are very important, as they control mood, memory, focus and concentration, sleep, and many more processes needed to function normally. Proteins are most commonly found in animal products such as meat, poultry, fish, and dairy. It is possible to replace these sources if you follow a vegan or vegetarian diet. Still, it will require careful planning and consideration to ensure you do not suffer from protein deficiency. Likewise, not all fats are healthy or conducive to brain development.

Still, the idea that all fats are bad is also a misconception. Certain fats are healthy and necessary for healthy brain and body function. A deficiency in healthy fats has been linked to depression. The most healthy fats to consume are the ones found in avocados, nuts, seeds, coconut oil, olives, and fatty fish. Vegetable oils such as canola, safflower, and soy are called trans fats and are unhealthy. It is best to avoid these, as they can negatively affect your physical and brain health. Finally, the same can be said of carbohydrates—they are not all unhealthy. Carbohydrates are an essential energy source, but refined carbohydrates are not sustainable and cause a "crash" in energy levels not long after consumption. They are often associated with high blood sugar levels and can increase your risk of developing diabetes. This is why we need to focus on eating unrefined or complex carbohydrates. These carbs can be found in starchy vegetables such as carrots, beets, yams, potatoes, and squash. These healthy carbs will energize your brain and body and sustain energy levels throughout the day.

Micronutrients

There are several micronutrients that the body needs to promote optimal health and functioning. Unfortunately, people who suffer from malnutrition are likely to suffer deficiencies in micronutrients rather than macronutrients. For example, omega-3 fatty acids are important micronutrients our bodies need to function. These fatty acids benefit brain development, promoting brain growth and improving cognitive function. Omega-3 consists of three main fatty acids, namely alpha-linolenic acid (ALA), docosahexaenoic acid (DHA), and eicosapentaenoic acid (EPA). These fatty acids are associated with improved memory and concentration, better mood regulation, and a lowered risk of developing Alzheimer's disease. Antioxidants are another micronutrient that is necessary for brain health. Antioxidants have many benefits for the body. Some of these include slowing aging and protecting the body against free-radical damage.

B vitamins are sometimes called "happy vitamins" because they help to improve mood and reduce stress. In addition, they are beneficial to improving cognitive health and function and boosting neurotransmitter production. Thus, they help the brain form stronger connections between neurons and can help in preventing neurodegenerative diseases. There are eight B vitamins, the most important being B-12. Vitamin B-12 is one of the B vitamins many people lack. It can lead to severe problems such as memory loss, fatigue, mental confusion, nerve damage, and weakness. Vegetarians and vegans are especially at risk of developing vitamin b-12 deficiency, as it is only found in animal products. Thus, they need to take supplements to make up for this deficiency. Vitamin D is another important micronutrient. Many people suffer from a deficiency due to significantly reduced time spent outside. Consuming vitamin D can help improve memory and mood and prevent cognitive decline. Due to the nature of our lifestyles, taking a vitamin D supplement may be beneficial. Magnesium is another nutrient that many people lack. Magnesium provides a better mood, concentration, sleep, reduced cravings, energy, and stress management.

INTERMITTENT FASTING

Diet fads and trends have consumed social media and the world, and every day there is a new theory of which foods and nutrients are good for your health. This can be confusing and upsetting for someone who is neither a doctor nor a nutritionist. Be careful of grappling with the first new diet fad that you see. These fads may produce results and look effective, but physical appearance can be deceiving. Intermittent fasting is one of the dietary lifestyles that have been the subject of study and have proven to have positive results for brain health. This is a practice whereby people restrict their eating to certain times of the day, thus restricting *when* a person should eat rather than *what* they should eat. People take different approaches to this method, but the three most commonly used methods exist. The 16/8 method involves skipping breakfast, allowing for nine hours of eating time, and then 16 hours of fasting. The second type, eat-stop-eat, involves a 24-hour fast once or twice every week. The third method is the 5:2 method, whereby a person eats normally for five days a week and consumes only 500 to 600 calories daily on the remaining two days. These two days must be non-consecutive.

There is much contestation and speculation about fasting. Still, intermittent fasting has shown many benefits—especially for brain health. Intermittent fasting has been shown to trigger a process known as autophagy–a process of detoxification that the brain undergoes at the end of every day. It, therefore, helps the brain to get rid of any old or damaged cells and clears the mind of unnecessary debris. Furthermore, intermittent fasting is associated with improved memory and mood and reduced inflammation. It also helps to regulate blood sugar and helps to lower blood pressure at night—a process conducive to better heart health. It has also been shown to burn excess fat, thus causing weight loss. Although the brain needs certain fats to function effectively, excess fat in the body is unhealthy. It can lead to various health risks involving physical and mental health.

HERBS AND SPICES FOR BRAIN HEALTH

Aside from the brain foods I have mentioned, certain herbs and spices can also improve brain health and cognition. Sage has been shown to improve memory and improve cognition. It can also help in reducing the risk of developing Alzheimer's disease. Sage can be enjoyed as a tea or is a wonderful addition to butternut, chicken, turkey, or certain soups. Turmeric is a yellow spice found in many curries that contains churchmen. Curcumin contains antioxidants that help to protect neurons and improve brain health. It is also known to have anti-inflammatory qualities. Ginkgo Biloba is a herb often used in Chinese traditional medicine that stimulates circulation and increases blood flow to the brain. It is also linked with slowing down neurodegeneration. Ashwagandha is a shrub traditionally used in Indian medicine and can help reduce oxidative stress and the risk of Alzheimer's disease. Ginseng is another spice related to improved memory and even prevents memory loss. It contains ginsenosides, which help slow mental decline and prevent neurodegenerative diseases. Gotu Kola has also been used in alternative forms of medicine and is often associated with improved mental clarity. It helps to reduce oxidative stress and slow down cognitive decline. Lemon balm is generally consumed in tea form and helps to ease anxiety and insomnia. It can also prevent memory loss and improve cognitive function. If you can afford it, saffron is also rich in antioxidants, thus helping to protect the brain. Rosemary has been shown to improve memory, prevent brain cell death and slow down neurodegeneration. Cinnamon can improve blood circulation and help regulate blood sugar levels.

Nutmeg, ginger, and pepper are also goo
and can help improve cognition.

THE IMPORTANCE OF WATER

Water is often forgotten in dietary planning and even exercise. Drinking enough water is essential for physical health and bodily function, effective cognition, and brain health. The body consists of around 80 percent water. In comparison, the brain consists of 73 percent water, thus indicating the importance of water in bodily and cognitive functioning. Water is necessary for the process of producing hormones and neurotransmitters. Dehydration can harm various aspects and functions of the brain, including memory and concentration. It has also been linked to more negative moods. Dehydration has been associated with symptoms such as fatigue, irregular sleep, depression, brain fog, and a lack of focus. It is, therefore, very important to ensure that you are oxygenated and hydrated at all times to ensure optimal brain function. By staying hydrated, you can focus better and experience more mental clarity.

CAFFEINE

I have mentioned coffee as one of the brain foods in my discussion above, partly because of the caffeine it contains. Many people have labeled caffeine as a bad substance that should be avoided at all costs, and this is simply not true. Caffeine may be detrimental to some people

. certain conditions but has shown several benefits for .ain health and development. For example, it helps to speed up reaction time, improves mood, and increases attention and vigilance. Although caffeine does not directly impact the brain itself, its effects on these factors can help improve cognition.

NOOTROPICS

Nootropics, sometimes called smart drugs, are developed for and directed toward cognitive enhancement. There are three broad categories of nootropics—stimulant drugs, synthetic compounds, and natural compounds. Stimulant drugs are directed toward boosting awareness and improving concentration. These are substances, such as Adderall and Ritalin, that are commonly prescribed for people with ADHD. These stimulants raise dopamine levels in the brain, leading to increased attention span, alertness, and energy levels. Synthetic compounds target the neurotransmitters known as glutamate and acetylcholine. The most common form of synthetic compounds is racetams, which are used to boost the memory of people with brain injuries or age-related cognitive decline. These substances have no known impact on healthy individuals. Natural compounds are substances such as caffeine, herbal ginseng, and creatine. These are the most popular drugs for neurological enhancement and stimulation and can be bought over the counter.

Some people use stimulant drugs as a neurological enhancer rather than a treatment for ADHD. Although it has shown promising effects on concentration and focus, it can harm your body. The use of stimulants can cause side effects such as insomnia, increased heart rate, increased risk of stroke, hallucinations, and even addiction in some cases. Natural or synthetic compounds are considered safe when used in moderation or according to guidelines. However, these nootropics have pros and cons, and these should be carefully considered before deciding whether to take them. Synthetic compounds are generally stronger and, therefore, more effective. They are also readily available at many pharmacies, stores, or online. However, some synthetic compounds require a prescription, and certain compounds, such as creatine, have been the subject of ethical contestation and debate. Although not as strong and effective as synthetic compounds, natural compounds are generally safer to use. They are generally easy to access and require no prescription. They also come with fewer risks and side effects compared to synthetic compounds.

Herbal nootropics are plants and herbs that have brain-enhancing qualities. These herbs fall under the category of natural compounds, but not all natural  compounds are herbal. Many of the herbs used as nootropics have been used by ancient civilizations and in traditional medicine for centuries. Some of the most effective herbal nootropics are ashwagandha, bacopa monnieri, CBD oils, ginkgo biloba, ginseng, gotu kola, holy basil, lemon balm, l-theanine, maca, saffron, rhodiola rosea, turmeric, vinpocetine, and valerian. As with all things, moderation is important. If you take these herbal nootropics, follow the dosage instructions or consult your medical practitioner as necessary.

LION'S MANE MUSHROOMS

Lion's mane mushrooms have been used in traditional Chinese medicine for years. These are cream-colored, slightly hairy mushrooms, as seen below. This mushroom has been shown to increase neuron development and growth, thus indicating that it may benefit brain health and development. Studies have not confirmed whether it is, in fact, beneficial or safe for humans to use lion's mane for neurological enhancement. Still, studies and trials are being conducted on Alzheimer's patients to evaluate its effect on memory enhancement. These mushrooms have been linked to many health benefits, such as increased immunity, reduced anxiety and depression, better inflammation regulation, improved heart health, and increased resistance to diabetes. However, these findings have all been based on animal studies and have not been confirmed with certainty.

Some countless foods and supplements can improve brain development and function. They can be beneficial to our physical and brain health. The last thing we need to consider is emotional intelligence to help us process our emotions and thoughts and communicate these in a way that is healthy and beneficial to our mental health.

1 0

EMOTIONAL INTELLIGENCE

Y ou may have heard of IQ or intelligence quotient. This is used to measure intelligence in people to compare how smart they are. It is widely known, however, that people with high levels of intelligence cannot empathize and socialize with the people around them.

Daniel Goleman, author of the book titled *Emotional Intelligence: Why it can matter more than IQ*, writes that "Socrates's injunction 'Know thyself' speaks to the keystone of emotional intelligence: awareness of one's feelings as they occur."

Possessing knowledge and information and being able to solve complex equations is simply not enough, as it does not offer us the ability to work through complex emotions or establish and maintain meaningful relationships. This is why developing a healthy brain also involves developing a high EQ, or emotional quotient, along with our IQ.

WHAT IS EMOTIONAL INTELLIGENCE?

Emotional intelligence, or EQ, refers to one's ability to understand and manage your own emotions while also being able to understand and empathize with others. Knowledge and information can be obtained and mastered through study, and consistent exposure to such information, but emotional intelligence is more challenging to conquer. Developing emotional intelligence is truly an act of self-mastery and understanding. People with high levels of emotional intelligence are often characterized by self-confidence and self-acceptance, showing empathy and understanding toward others, and being able to take responsibility for, accept, and move on from their mistakes. Emotional intelligence can, in some respects, be more important than IQ for success in life. Emotional intelligence involves four levels. Firstly, it requires the ability to perceive or identify emotions accurately. This involves not only the ability to listen but also requires an understanding of nonverbal cues such as facial expressions and body language. The second level involves the ability to reason with emotions. We cannot always trust and believe what we feel. Therefore we need to be able to differentiate and prioritize which emotions we give our attention to. Next, we need to possess an understanding of emotions. Once we can identify emotions, we must interpret their meaning and where they come from. These are important aspects to consider before attempting to solve the issue. Finally, emotional intelligence requires us to manage our emotions. This involves regulating our emotions and responding to them in a reasonable and fair way. This requires a higher level of maturity and development but is very beneficial to emotional and brain health.

COMPONENTS OF EMOTIONAL INTELLIGENCE

Five main aspects make up emotional intelligence. Firstly, EQ requires a higher level of self-awareness. Self-awareness involves being aware of one's emotional state and feelings consistently. Not only that, but an emotionally intelligent person can also communicate these feelings effectively. Self-awareness involves knowing when certain emotions occur and how they can impact you. Once people become aware of their emotional state, they can focus on mastering self-regulation. This involves managing your emotions and better controlling your behaviors amid these emotions. Resisting impulsive actions and decisions amid intense emotion is an important skill to master. It will benefit you in all areas of life. The third component, motivation, is important to aiming and working toward certain important goals in life. Motivation is an essential aspect that fuels everything we do and strives for and enables us to push on amid trials and setbacks. Emotional intelligence also requires empathy—the ability to be in tune with others' emotions. Despite common confusion, empathy and sympathy are not the same. Where sympathy says: "Oh shame," offers a pat on the back, and moves on, empathy drives compassion. It involves feeling another person's emotions and putting yourself in their metaphorical shoes. Finally, emotional intelligence places a high value on social skills. Emotional intelligence requires an understanding of how to interact with and understand people. These components present many advantages in developing relationships and building a successful life.

Emotional intelligence can be a tremendous asset and will undoubtedly contribute to developing a more successful and meaningful life. It will lead to a more fulfilling work life, better meaningful relationships, and improved mental and physical health. In addition, developing your emotional intelligence will help you manage stress more effectively, improve your overall mood, better express yourself, and help you develop your understanding of emotions and emotional regulation. Higher levels of emotional intelligence will also increase your overall life satisfaction, leaving you happier and less stressed than ever.

HOW TO DEVELOP AND IMPROVE EMOTIONAL INTELLIGENCE

If emotional intelligence is not something you think you have, there is no need to worry. Emotional intelligence can be developed and improved with practice; the more you practice, the better you will do. Remember that, as with all things, practice takes time. When you do these exercises and take these steps, keep working on them, and do not be discouraged by failure. Failure is a necessary step on the road to success. The more you practice, the closer you will become to improving your emotional intelligence. Some basic things you can practice daily to improve your emotional intelligence are to be aware of and reflect on your emotions and pause to think before speaking. This teaches your brain not to simply react out of a certain emotion but to learn to differentiate and consider your actions. Ask others for their opinion or perspective, and when you face criticism, ask yourself what you can learn from it and how you can improve. When others react differently to the way you expected, consider their position and ask yourself what they might be feeling and why they may be reacting in this way.

Another way to develop your emotional intelligence is to assume that the people around us have only positive intentions. Miscommunications can happen easily, and we often take criticism as a personal attack. Try to look for the positive or constructive in what the people around you say or do rather than searching for every criticism you can find. This will promote a positive mental attitude and help you identify areas that need improvement, ultimately making you a better person. Listening without interruption is an effective way to develop empathy and understanding, an important aspect of emotional intelligence. We quickly jump to conclusions, finishing each other's thoughts and sentences before they have a chance. To develop true empathy and understanding, it is important to listen, *really* listen, when others are speaking.

Emotional intelligence is an important aspect of mental health, not only because it promotes success but because it can make your life more meaningful and fulfilling. Developing your emotional intelligence will enable you to be less sensitive toward criticism, to deal more effectively with stress, and to manage relationships more easily. It will inadvertently also give you more self-confidence and self-assurance, helping you trust your decision-making skills and abilities. These keys to a healthier and more fulfilling life will set you up for success.

If you enjoyed this book, please consider leaving a review.

AFTERWORD

The brain is a powerful, intricate, and complex tool that can benefit us if we look after it. A healthy brain can do more than you ever imagined your brain can do. The brain is complex and intricate in how it functions and communicates with the rest of the body. It is responsible for every thought, emotion, and action we take. If we take better care of our brains, it will inevitably influence the way we think, feel, and act. Due to its neuroplasticity and learning ability, we can change our brains by reprogramming how we think and respond. Our brain does not stop developing, and it is never too late for us to influence our brain. We need to ensure that we look after our brains and promote a healthy brain by getting enough sleep and exercise, following a healthy diet, and socializing with others. In doing so, we not only prevent our brains from degenerating, but we strengthen the connections in our brains, helping us think better and keeping us healthier for longer. In taking care of our brain, it is also important to avoid stress where possible and to deal with the stress that we face. Not all stress is bad, but it can become detrimental if it persists and is not dealt with appropriately. We need to establish healthy and conducive relationships and maintain a healthy lifestyle to ensure that we can deal with the worries and stresses that life throws our way and to better enable ourselves to establish a meaningful life. Focusing on our diet and including certain brain foods can boost our brain performance and protect us from neurode-generation. We must ensure that we eat enough healthy food and stay hydrated. This will benefit us in the long run. Finally, we need to ensure that we develop not only our IQ but also our EQ. Doing so will help us to manage our emotions, stresses, and environments more effectively and improve our chances of experiencing success. Once you implement these steps, you will enable yourself to build a better and more satisfactory life.

I would like to share a real-life story of triumph and success to show you the reality of our brain's ability to change and adapt. This story was told by Will Storr (2015) in one of his articles on the magnificence of the brain. Storr tells of a woman, Debbie Hampton, who was tired of her life and felt like she had failed miserably. And so, in 2007, she attempted to commit suicide. She was found by paramedics and rushed to the hospital, but had already been brain damaged. Debbie woke up unable to swallow or speak properly, having no control over her bladder, her hands shook violently, and she had difficulty interpreting visual information. She went through rehabilitation and was able to experience some improvement. Still, after one year, she no longer noticed any improvements. She could speak, but her speech was slow and slurry. Her memory was faulty, and her energy levels were very low. It seemed like this was the best she would get from her life. She then started a neurofeedback treatment, which helps patients master self-control by monitoring brainwave activity and sending feedback. After ten sessions of this therapy, she was able to gain back her speech. She then started reading a book on neuroplasticity and brain health, after which she adopted a lifestyle conducive to brain health that included yoga, meditation, visualization, and a healthy diet. She also worked on developing and keeping a positive attitude. She is now living a functional life where she co-owns a yoga studio and has even written an autobiography. She advocates for brain health and spreads awareness about neuroplasticity. You may not have experienced brain damage, but the same life-changing difference awaits you.

If you are tired of fatigue, brain fog, and memory loss, and you are tired of not reaching your potential, then I hope you will take what you have learned throughout this book and apply it to your life. This is not a book that you read and then put aside. Reading this book is not automatically going to change your life. Knowledge is power only if newfound knowledge is used to make improvements and adjustments where necessary. It requires deliberate and focused action—only then will it begin to make a difference. It does not have to happen all at once, but you must take a deliberate step toward improving your brain health. Form a plan of action in which you implement all you have learned, chapter by chapter, systematically until you have improved each of these areas. Remember that it is not a quick fix. It will not change all at once, and you will, without a doubt, falter sometimes and in some areas. The important thing is to be intentional about what you do and how you live from now on and that you keep working toward the goal. You have been given all the tools and information you could need to foster a healthy brain and build a more meaningful life. The proverbial ball is now in your court—what will you do with it?

GLOSSARY

Brain-Derived Neurotrophic Factor (BNDF): A protein that is found in the brain and spinal cord, which promotes the survival and growth of neurons in the brain.

Central Nervous System (CNS): The body's information processing center, which is made up of the brain and the spinal cord.

Dopamine: A chemical found in the body most often associated with pleasure, but also contributing to memory, attention span, learning, and motivation.

Enteric Nervous System (ENS): A series of neurons found in the gastrointestinal system, which controls digestive functions.

Long-Term Potentiation (LTP): The strengthening of existing connections between neurons in the body.

Meninges: Three membranes that line and protect the central nervous system.

Metacognition: Being aware of one's thought processes and understanding.

Myelin: A protective layer that forms around the nerves to protect and insulate the nerves.

Neurons: Also called a nerve cell. These cells communicate messages between the brain and the body using electrical currents.

Neuroplasticity: The brain's ability to change physically and form itself to adapt and learn throughout the course of life.

Norepinephrine: A naturally occurring chemical in the body that triggers the body's fight-or-flight response and prepares it for survival.

Rapid Eye Movement (REM): A phase during the sleep cycle where eye movement is visible, and dreaming, bodily movement, rapid breathing, and increased pulse are most likely.

Serotonin: A chemical that is released into the body that helps with mood regulation and -stabilization.

Synaptogenesis: The formation of new connections between neurons in the body.

Visual Categorization: The brain's ability to organize visual information and objects into distinct categories.

BIBLIOGRAPHY

7 incredible things intermittent fasting does for your brain. (2020, March 2). Amen Clinics. Retrieved April 2, 2023, from https://www.amenclinics.com/blog/7-incredible-things-intermittent-fasting-does-for-your-brain/

9 health benefits of music. (2020, December 31). North Shore. Retrieved March 30, 2023, from https://www.northshore.org/healthy-you/9-health-benefits-of-music/

36.2: Sensory Processes - Transduction and Perception. (2022, June 9). Biology LibreTexts. Retrieved March 29, 2023, from https://bio.libretexts.org/Bookshelves/Introductory_and_General_Biology/Book%3A_General_Biology_(Boundless)/36%3A_Sensory_Systems/36.02%3A_Sensory_Processes_-_Transduction_and_Perception

Ackerman, C. E., MA. (2019, February 4). *13 emotional intelligence activities, exercises & PDFs*. Positive Psychology. Retrieved March 29, 2023, from https://positivepsychology.com/emotional-intelligence-exercises/

Adan, A. (2012). *Cognitive performance and dehydration*. Journal of the American College of Nutrition, 31(2), 71–78. https://doi.org/10.1080/07315724.2012.10720011

Alban, P. (2022, December 19). *Essential nutrients for a healthy brain*. Be Brain Fit. Retrieved April 3, 2023, from https://bebrainfit.com/brain-nutrients/

Amino acid: Benefits & food sources. (2021, November 12). Cleveland Clinic. Retrieved April 4, 2023, from https://my.clevelandclinic.org/health/articles/22243-amino-acids

Avramova, N. (2019, February 20). *How music can change the way you feel and act*. CNN. Retrieved April 2, 2023, from https://edition.cnn.com/2019/02/08/health/music-brain-behavior-intl/index.html

Baluch, P., & Gonzales, A. (n.d.). *How do we see?* Arizona State University. Retrieved March 31, 2023, from https://askabiologist.asu.edu/explore/how-do-we-see

BDNF gene. (n.d.). Medline Plus. Retrieved April 5, 2023, from https://medlineplus.gov/genetics/gene/bdnf/

Berry, J. (2019, September 18). *What are nootropics (smart drugs)?* Medical News Today. Retrieved April 4, 2023, from https://www.medicalnewstoday.com/articles/326379

Bill Engvall quote. (n.d.). A-Z Quotes. Retrieved March 29, 2023, from https://www.azquotes.com/quote/1401935

Brain anatomy and how the brain works. (2021, July 14). Johns Hopkins Medicine. Retrieved March 23, 2023, from https://www.hopkinsmedicine.org/health/conditions-and-diseases/anatomy-of-the-brain

Brainstem. (2021, June 21). Cleveland Clinic. Retrieved March 22, 2023, from https://my.clevelandclinic.org/health/body/21598-brainstem

Brown, H., PhD. (2021, October 7). *What is nature and ecotherapy & how does it work?* Positive Psychology. Retrieved March 23, 2023, from https://positivepsychology.com/nature-therapy/

Cahn, L. (2022, March 16). *Bad stress vs. Good stress: How to know the difference.* The Healthy. Retrieved March 31, 2023, from https://www.thehealthy.com/mental-health/stress/bad-stress-vs-good-stress-how-to-know-the-difference/

Carl Sagan quotes. (n.d.). BrainyQuote. Retrieved April 4, 2023, from https://www.brainyquote.com/quotes/carl_sagan_125868?src=t_brain

Cassata, C. (2023, February 13). *What is norepinephrine?* Everyday Health. Retrieved April 2, 2023, from https://www.everydayhealth.com/norepinephrine/guide/

Cerebral cortex. (2022, May 23). Cleveland Clinic. Retrieved April 3, 2023, from https://my.clevelandclinic.org/health/articles/23073-cerebral-cortex#:~:text=Collectively%2C%20your%20cerebral%20cortex%20is,%2C%20emotion%2C%20intelligence%20and%20personality.

Charvat, M. (2019, January 7). *Why exercise is good for your brain.* Psychology Today. Retrieved March 26, 2023, from https://www.psychologytoday.com/us/blog/the-fifth-vital-sign/201901/why-exercise-is-good-your-brain

Cherry, K. (2021, April 8). *5 surprising ways that stress affects your brain.* Verywell Mind. Retrieved March 24, 2023, from https://www.verywellmind.com/surprising-ways-that-stress-affects-your-brain-2795040

Cherry, K. (2022a, November 7). *What is emotional intelligence?* Verywell Mind. Retrieved March 29, 2023, from https://www.verywellmind.com/what-is-emotional-intelligence-2795423

Cherry, K. (2022b, November 15). *Parts of the brain.* Verywell Mind. Retrieved March 25, 2023, from https://www.verywellmind.com/the-anatomy-of-the-brain-2794895

Cherry, K. (2023a, February 23). *Understanding body language and facial expressions.* Verywell Mind. Retrieved March 30, 2023, from https://www.verywellmind.com/understand-body-language-and-facial-expressions-4147228

Cherry, K. (2023b, March 2). *What is consciousness?* Verywell Mind. Retrieved March 28, 2023, from https://www.verywellmind.com/what-is-consciousness-2795922

Cohut, M., PhD. (2018, February 23). *What are the health benefits of being social?* Medical News Today. Retrieved April 3, 2023, from https://www.medicalnewstoday.com/articles/321019#_noHeaderPrefixedContent

Cohut, M., PhD. (2019, February 22). *How language shapes our brains. . .and our lives.* Medical News Today. Retrieved April 3, 2023, from https://www.medicalnewstoday.com/articles/324529

Cole, N. L. (2020, January 30). *Understanding socialization in sociology.* Thought Co. Retrieved March 25, 2023, from https://www.thoughtco.com/socialization-in-sociology-4104466

Cotman, C. W., & Berchtold, N. C. (2002). *Exercise: a behavioral intervention to enhance brain health and plasticity.* Trends in Neurosciences, 25(6), 295–301. https://doi.org/10.1016/s0166-2236(02)02143-4

Cuncic, A. (2023, March 28). *How to read facial expressions.* Verywell Mind. Retrieved April 2, 2023, from https://www.verywellmind.com/understanding-emotions-through-facial-expressions-3024851

Cunnington, R. (2019, September 18). *Neuroplasticity: How the brain changes with learning.* Science of Learning Portal. Retrieved March 17, 2023, from https://solportal.ibe-unesco.org/articles/neuroplasticity-how-the-brain-changes-with-learning/

Dam, R. F. (n.d.). *Social evolution and why we need to communicate.* The Interaction Design Foundation. Retrieved April 2, 2023, from https://www.interaction-design.org/literature/article/social-evolution-and-why-we-need-to-communicate

Daniel Goleman quotes. (n.d.). Goodreads. Retrieved April 3, 2023, from https://www.goodreads.com/author/quotes/829.Daniel_Goleman

Deal, H. (2021, October 20). *Ultimate guide to nootropics in 2023: Everything you need to know about nootropics.* Green Nootropics. Retrieved March 24, 2023, from https://greennootropics.com/blog/ultimate-guide-to-nootropics/#Pros_Vs_Cons_Of_Natural_and_Synthetic_Nootropics

Dopamine. (2022, March 23). Cleveland Clinic. Retrieved March 29, 2023, from https://my.clevelandclinic.org/health/articles/22581-dopamine

Edlund, M. J. (2016, July 23). *Is the brain like muscle?* Psychology Today. Retrieved April 4, 2023, from https://www.psychologytoday.com/us/blog/getting-healthy-now/201607/is-the-brain-muscle

Ekstrand, B., Scheers, N., Rasmussen, M. K., Young, J. F., Ross, A. B., & Landberg, R. (2021). *Brain foods - the role of diet in brain performance and health.*

Nutrition Reviews, 79(6), 693–708. https://doi.org/10.1093/nutrit/nuaa091

Experts review evidence yoga is good for the brain. (2019, December 12). Science Daily. Retrieved April 4, 2023, from https://www.sciencedaily.com/releases/2019/12/191212105851.htm

Eye expressions offer a glimpse into the evolution of emotion. (2017, April 17). Science Daily. Retrieved April 4, 2023, from https://www.sciencedaily.com/releases/2017/04/170417182822.htm

Eysenck, M. W., & Keane, M. T. (2015). *Cognitive Psychology: A Student's Handbook.* Psychology Press.

F. (2021, August 9). *How dehydration affects your brain.* Fayaz Neuro Surgery. Retrieved April 2, 2023, from https://fayazneurosurgery.com/how-dehydration-affects-your-brain/#:~:text=A%202%25%20decrease%20in%20brain, have%20been%20dehydrated%20for%20years.&text=Lack%20of%20mental%20clarity%2C%20sometimes,to%20as%20%E2%80%9Cbrain%20-fog.%E2%80%9D

Flynn, H. (2023, February 17). *Improving memory: Lion's mane mushrooms may double neuron growth.* https://www.medicalnewstoday.com/articles/improving-memory-lions-mane-mushrooms-may-double-neuron-growth

Foods linked to better brainpower. (2021, March 6). Harvard Health. Retrieved April 2, 2023, from https://www.health.harvard.edu/healthbeat/foods-linked-to-better-brainpower

Glasshouse, N. (2017, August 10). *Why brain training is important.* Conscious Float. Retrieved March 24, 2023, from https://consciousfloat.com/why-brain-training-is-important/

Gothe, N. P., Khan, I., Hayes, J. S., Erlenbach, E., & Damoiseaux, J. S. (2019). *Yoga effects on brain health: A systematic review of the current literature.* Brain Plasticity, 5(1), 105–122. https://doi.org/10.3233/bpl-190084

Gray and white matter of the brain. (2022, January 23). Medline Plus. Retrieved March 20, 2023, from https://medlineplus.gov/ency/imagepages/18117.htm#:~:text=The%20tissue%20called%20%22gray%20matter,is%20composed%20of%20nerve%20fibers.

Greene, P. (2022, October 17). *11 types of animals without brains.* Wildlife Informer. Retrieved March 23, 2023, from https://wildlifeinformer.com/animals-without-brains/

Gunnars, K. (2022, June 16). *Intermittent fasting 101 — The ultimate beginner's guide.* Healthline. Retrieved March 22, 2023, from https://www.healthline.com/nutrition/intermittent-fasting-guide

Hasson, U. (2022, October 16). *This is your brain on communication.* ideas.ted.-

com. Retrieved March 19, 2023, from https://ideas.ted.com/this-is-your-brain-on-communication/

Hernandez, C. (2019, May 15). *Heliotherapy: Benefits of the sun far and beyond vitamin D.* The Healthy Home Economist. Retrieved March 18, 2023, from https://www.thehealthyhomeeconomist.com/heliotherapy-benefits-of-the-sun-beyond-vitamin-d/

Holland, K. (2019, March 14). *7 Ways to Keep Your Brain Healthy.* Healthline. Retrieved March 25, 2023, from https://www.healthline.com/health-news/heres-how-to-keep-your-brain-healthy-as-you-age

Holland, K. (2022, March 1). *Sensory processing disorder: Understanding sensory issues in children.* Healthline. Retrieved March 19, 2023, from https://www.healthline.com/health/childrens-health/sensory-issues-in-children#sensory-processing

Hood, B., PhD. (2019, June 14). *Why do we need a brain?* Psychology Today. Retrieved March 28, 2023, from https://www.psychologytoday.com/us/blog/the-self-illusion/201204/why-do-we-need-brain

How the brain integrates sensory input. (2019, April 30). Science Daily. Retrieved March 22, 2023, from https://www.sciencedaily.com/releases/2019/04/190430121757.htm

Hutmacher, F. (2021). *What Is Our Most Important Sense?* Frontiers for Young Minds, 9. https://doi.org/10.3389/frym.2021.548120

Importance of sensory integration. (n.d.). Pathways. Retrieved March 29, 2023, from https://pathways.org/wp-content/uploads/2014/10/understanding-the-senses-1.pdf

Jasper. (2019, November 12). *Why brain training is not something you should miss out on.* Brain Gymmer. Retrieved March 23, 2023, from https://www.braingymmer.com/en/blog/why-brain-training/

Jennings, K. (2021, June 21). *11 best foods to boost your brain and memory.* Healthline. Retrieved March 14, 2023, from https://www.healthline.com/nutrition/11-brain-foods

Jiang, K. (2016, January 29). *Learning how the brain learns.* UChicago Medicine. Retrieved March 26, 2023, from https://www.uchicagomedicine.org/forefront/neurosciences-articles/learning-how-the-brain-learns

Johnson, J. (2020, July 10). *What to know about animal therapy.* Medical News Today. Retrieved April 6, 2023, from https://www.medicalnewstoday.com/articles/animal-therapy

Kamrani, P., Marston, G., Arbor, T. C., & Jan, A. (2023, March 5). *Anatomy, connective tissue.* National Library of Medicine. Retrieved March 26, 2023, from https://www.ncbi.nlm.nih.gov/books/NBK538534/

Keep your brain young with music. (n.d.). Johns Hopkins Medicine. Retrieved

March 19, 2023, from https://www.hopkinsmedicine.org/health/well-ness-and-prevention/keep-your-brain-young-with-music#:~:text=Research%20has%20shown%20that%20listening, %2C%20mental%20alertness%2C%20and%20memory.

Kelly, M. (2021, July 9). *100 Communication Quotes To Remind You How Powerful It Is.* Goalcast. https://www.goalcast.com/communication-quotes/

Kingsland, J. (2023, January 21). *How does the human brain create consciousness, and why?* Medical News Today. Retrieved March 18, 2023, from https://www.medicalnewstoday.com/articles/how-does-the-human-brain-create-consciousness-and-why

Klemm, W. R., PhD. (2020, January 7). *How does learning change the brain?* Psychology Today. Retrieved March 20, 2023, from https://www.psychologytoday.com/us/blog/memory-medic/202001/how-does-learning-change-the-brain

Koltuska-Haskin, B. (2022, May 31). *Yoga and the brain.* Psychology Today. Retrieved April 4, 2023, from https://www.psychologytoday.com/us/blog/how-my-brain-works/202205/yoga-and-the-brain

Krockow, E. M. (2018, September 27). *How many decisions do we make each day?* Psychology Today. Retrieved March 18, 2023, from https://www.psychologytoday.com/za/blog/stretching-theory/201809/how-many-decisions-do-we-make-each-day

Kubala, J., & Jennings, K. (2022, January 20). *15 simple ways to relieve stress.* Healthline. Retrieved March 24, 2023, from https://www.healthline.com/nutrition/16-ways-relieve-stress-anxiety

Lewin, J. (2022, November 24). *10 foods to boost your brainpower.* BBC Good Food. Retrieved March 23, 2023, from https://www.bbcgoodfood.com/howto/guide/10-foods-boost-your-brainpower

Lewis, T., & Taylor, A. P. (2021, May 28). *Human brain: Facts, functions & anatomy.* livescience.com. https://www.livescience.com/29365-human-brain.html

Lindberg, S. (2019, August 7). *13 Brain Exercises to Help Keep You Mentally Sharp.* Healthline. https://www.healthline.com/health/mental-health/brain-exercises

Lockett, E. (2022, August 19). *Understanding sensory integration.* Healthline. Retrieved March 20, 2023, from https://www.healthline.com/health/autism/sensory-integration#diagnosis

Lynch, M. (2018, October 25). *How brain-based learning makes a difference.* The Edvocate. Retrieved April 3, 2023, from https://www.theedadvocate.org/how-brain-based-learning-makes-a-difference/

Martyn Bassett Associates. (n.d.). *10 ways to improve your emotional intelligence*

(EQ). Martyn Bassett Associates Inc. Retrieved March 24, 2023, from https://www.mbassett.com/blog/10-ways-to-improve-your-emotional-intelligence-eq

Masento, N., Golightly, M., Field, D., Butler, L. T., & Van Reekum, C. M. (2014). *Effects of hydration status on cognitive performance and mood.* British Journal of Nutrition, 111(10), 1841–1852. https://doi.org/10.1017/s0007114513004455

Mental Floss UK. (2017, February 10). *How our eyes see everything upside down.* Mental Floss. Retrieved March 14, 2023, from https://www.mentalfloss.com/article/91177/how-our-eyes-see-everything-upside-down

Mier, J. D. (2021, May 17). *Why and how heliotherapy can be used to treat skin disease and depression?.* Heliotherapy Research Institute. Retrieved March 20, 2023, from https://heliotherapy.institute/what-is-heliotherapy/

Morsella, E., PhD. (2022, October 9). *The first 4 fundamentals about consciousness and the brain.* Psychology Today. Retrieved March 20, 2023, from https://www.psychologytoday.com/us/blog/consciousness-and-the-brain/202210/the-first-4-fundamentals-about-consciousness-and-the-brain

Murphy-Royal, C. (2016, July 22). *Do we really need a brain?* HeadStuff. Retrieved March 30, 2023, from https://headstuff.org/topical/science/really-need-brain/

Narayana Health Care. (2020, January 10). *Best diets for brain health by neurologists.* Narayana Health. Retrieved April 5, 2023, from https://www.narayanahealth.org/blog/best-diets-for-brain-health-by-neurologists/

Nootropics. (n.d.). Psychology Today. Retrieved April 6, 2023, from https://www.psychologytoday.com/us/basics/nootropics

Powell, J. (2020, July 3). *Music: How it affects your brain, changes your mood and helps you focus.* Science Focus. Retrieved March 18, 2023, from https://www.sciencefocus.com/the-human-body/music-science-brain-mood-focus/

Promind Build Admin. (2022, January 8). *Herbal nootropics - everything you need to know.* Promind Build. Retrieved March 29, 2023, from https://promindbuild.com/herbal-nootropics/

Psychology Today. (n.d.). *Understanding dreams.* Retrieved March 25, 2023, from https://www.psychologytoday.com/us/basics/sleep/understanding-dreams

Robinson, A. (2014, October 12). *How to keep your brain healthy.* The Guardian. Retrieved March 18, 2023, from https://www.theguardian.com/lifeandstyle/2014/oct/12/how-to-keep-your-brain-healthy-nobel-prize-medicine

Robinson, B. E. (2020, October 26). *How social connections improve your brain health.* Psychology Today. Retrieved March 27, 2023, from https://www.psychologytoday.com/us/blog/the-right-mind-set/202010/how-social-connections-improve-your-brain-health

Roth, G., & Dicke, U. (2005). *Evolution of the brain and intelligence.* Trends in Cognitive Sciences, 9(5), 250–257. https://doi.org/10.1016/j.tics.2005.03.005

Santos-Longhurst, A. (2019, April 8). *What Is the Physical Composition of the Human Brain?* Healthline. https://www.healthline.com/health/is-the-brain-a-muscle

Sarmah, A. (2019, February 8). *What is consciousness? 3 states and 5 functions of the conscious mind.* MindWiper. https://mindwiper.com/what-is-consciousness/

Scaccia, A. (2022, September 26). *Everything You Need to Know About Serotonin.* Healthline. Retrieved March 16, 2023, from https://www.healthline.com/health/mental-health/serotonin#functions

Schwarzlose, R. (2021, August 9). *3 ways the brain makes sense of the world.* Psychology Today. Retrieved March 29, 2023, from https://www.psychologytoday.com/us/blog/brainscapes/202108/3-ways-the-brain-makes-sense-the-world

Scott, E., PhD. (2022, April 26). *Stress relief techniques for every type of stress.* Verywell Mind. Retrieved March 12, 2023, from https://www.verywellmind.com/types-of-stress-and-stress-relief-techniques-3144482

Sensory Integration Quotes (2 quotes). (n.d.). https://www.goodreads.com/quotes/tag/sensory-integration

Shukla, A. (2019, August 6). *Brain-Based learning: Theory, strategies, and concepts.* Cognition Today. Retrieved April 5, 2023, from https://cognitiontoday.com/brain-based-learning-theory-strategies-and-concepts/

Spence, C. (2022, April 29). *How learning a new language changes your brain.* World of Better Learning. Retrieved April 5, 2023, from https://www.cambridge.org/elt/blog/2022/04/29/learning-language-changes-your-brain/

Spinal Cord. (2020, June 7). *Grey matter vs white matter in the brain.* Spinal Cord. Retrieved March 15, 2023, from https://www.spinalcord.com/blog/gray-matter-vs-white-matter-in-the-brain

Storr, W. (2022, February 24). *The brain's miracle superpowers of self-improvement.* BBC Future. https://www.bbc.com/future/article/20151123-the-brains-miracle-superpowers-of-self-improvement

Stress. (2022, March). Mind. Retrieved March 20, 2023, from https://www.-

mind.org.uk/information-support/types-of-mental-health-prob-
lems/stress/causes-of-stress/

Suttie, J. (2013, December 1). *Why you should sleep your way to the top.* Greater
Good Magazine. Retrieved March 18, 2023, from https://greater-
good.berkeley.edu/article/item/why_sleep_your_way_to_top

Sutton, J., PhD. (2023). *Consciousness in psychology: 8 theories & examples.* In
PositivePsychology.com. https://positivepsychology.com/consciousness-
psychology/

Tait, B. (2020, April 22). *Understanding the neuroscience behind emotional intelligence.* Forbes. Retrieved March 14, 2023, from https://www.forbes.-
com/sites/forbescoachescouncil/2020/04/22/understanding-the-
neuroscience-behind-emotional-intelligence/?sh=652619887623

Teitelbaum, J. (2016, September 12). *Communicate to the brain: The neuroscience
of communication.* My Tech Decisions. Retrieved April 2, 2023, from
https://mytechdecisions.com/compliance/communicate-brain-neuro-
science-communication/

Telloian, C. (2022, January 13). *How does stress affect the brain?* Psych Central.
Retrieved April 3, 2023, from https://psychcentral.com/stress/our-brain-
on-stress-forgetful-emotional

The 5 best physical exercises that support brain health. (2022, July 29). Mosh.
Retrieved March 24, 2023, from https://moshlife.com/blogs/wellness-
blog/best-physical-exercise-for-brain

The Brain-Gut connection. (2021, November 1). Johns Hopkins Medicine.
Retrieved April 2, 2023, from https://www.hopkinsmedi-
cine.org/health/wellness-and-prevention/the-brain-gut-connection

Thompson, V. (2022, October 11). *Famous quotes on sleep and well-Being.* Center
for the Advancement of Well-Being. Retrieved March 15, 2023, from
https://wellbeing.gmu.edu/famous-quotes-on-sleep-and-well-being/

Tiwari, D. (2021, February 26). *3 types of stress: Causes, effects & how to cope.*
Choosing Therapy. Retrieved March 28, 2023, from https://www.choos-
ingtherapy.com/types-of-stress/

Tocino-Smith, J. (2023, March 9). *10 neurological benefits of exercise.* Positive
Psychology. Retrieved March 22, 2023, from https://positivepsychology.-
com/exercise-neurological-benefits/

Tomen, D. (2023, April 4). *Best nootropic herbs.* https://nootropicsexpert.-
com/best-nootropic-herbs/

Top 25 quotes by Julie Garland. (n.d.). A-Z Quotes. Retrieved March 16, 2023,
from https://www.azquotes.com/author/5373-Julie_Garwood

Train your brain. (2021, February 15). Harvard Health. Retrieved April 3,

2023, from https://www.health.harvard.edu/mind-and-mood/train-your-brain

UAGC. (2021, December 8). *How does music affect your brain?* Retrieved March 22, 2023, from https://www.uagc.edu/blog/how-does-music-affect-your-brain

W, N. (2017, April 25). *Our eyes and brain. Relationship status: It's complicated.* Wu Tsai Neurosciences Institute. Retrieved March 17, 2023, from https://neuroscience.stanford.edu/news/our-eyes-and-brain-relation-ship-status-it-s-complicated

Walker, M. (2017, October 24). *Why your brain needs to dream.* Greater Good Science Center. Retrieved March 25, 2023, from https://greater-good.berkeley.edu/article/item/why_your_brain_needs_to_dream

Watson, S. (2009, June 19). *Causes of stress.* WebMD. Retrieved March 13, 2023, from https://www.webmd.com/balance/guide/causes-of-stress

Weaver, E. A., & Doyle, H. H. (2019, August 2). *How does exercise affect the brain?* Dana Foundation. Retrieved March 16, 2023, from https://www.-dana.org/article/how-does-exercise-affect-the-brain/

Wel, M. (2018, April 24). *Tai chi may improve brain health and muscle recovery.* Psychology Today. Retrieved April 4, 2023, from https://www.psycholo-gytoday.com/us/blog/urban-survival/201804/tai-chi-may-improve-brain-health-and-muscle-recovery

What are the 7 senses? (n.d.). 7 Senses Foundation. Retrieved March 13, 2023, from http://www.7senses.org.au/what-are-the-7-senses/

What is stress? (2022, March 30). The American Institute of Stress. Retrieved March 26, 2023, from https://www.stress.org/daily-life

What meditation can do for your mind, mood, and health. (2014, July 16). Harvard Health. Retrieved March 26, 2023, from https://www.health.harvard.e-du/staying-healthy/what-meditation-can-do-for-your-mind-mood-and-health-

Why brain training is important. (2021, November 15). A Cognitive Connec-tion. Retrieved March 31, 2023, from https://acognitiveconnection.-com/why-brain-training-is-important/

Why good vision is so important. (2017, October 16). Zeiss. Retrieved March 12, 2023, from https://www.zeiss.com/vision-care/us/better-vision/health-prevention/why-good-vision-is-so-important.html

Why multitasking doesn't work. (2021, March 10). Cleveland Clinic. Retrieved March 13, 2023, from https://health.clevelandclinic.org/science-clear-multitasking-doesnt-work/#:~:text=Multitasking%20can%20hin-der%20your%20performance&text=So%2Dcalled%20multitasking%20di-vides%20our,led%20to%20poorer%20driving%20performance.

Williams, F. (2022, May 30). *What to know about emotional intelligence.* https://www.medicalnewstoday.com/articles/components-of-emotional-intelligence

Wolf, A. (2020, August 8). *Tai chi: A Whole-Brain sensory integration.* The Brain Health Magazine. Retrieved March 12, 2023, from https://thebrain-healthmagazine.com/concussion/tai-chi/

Wong, C. (2023, March 22). *7 best herbs for memory and brain health.* Verywell Mind. Retrieved March 17, 2023, from https://www.verywellmind.com/best-herbs-and-spices-for-brain-health-4047818

Wood, J. D. (2004). *Enteric nervous system.* Science Direct. Retrieved March 27, 2023, from https://www.sciencedirect.com/topics/neuroscience/enteric-nervous-system

Your 8 senses. (n.d.). STAR Institute. Retrieved March 24, 2023, from https://sensoryhealth.org/basic/your-8-senses

Zoppi, L. (2022, January 28). *What to know about supplements for the brain.* https://www.medicalnewstoday.com/articles/best-brain-supplements

IMAGE REFERENCES

BrickBar. (2022, May 5). *Brain anatomy lobes medical.* Pixabay. https://pixabay.com/illustrations/brain-anatomy-lobes-medical-7174144/

Clker Free Vector Images. (2012, April 24). *Eye diagram.* Pixabay. https://pixabay.com/vectors/eye-diagram-eyeball-body-pupil-39998/

Clker-Free-Vector-Images. (2014, April 14). *Neuron nerve cell axon dendrite.* Pixabay. https://pixabay.com/vectors/neuron-nerve-cell-axon-dendrite-296581/

Doan, J. (2018, May 10). *Assorted sliced fruits in white ceramic bowl.* Pexels. https://www.pexels.com/photo/assorted-sliced-fruits-in-white-ceramic-bowl-1092730/

Elevate. (2018, July 26). *Four women chatting while sitting on bench.* Pexels. https://www.pexels.com/photo/four-women-chatting-while-sitting-on-bench-1267697/

Fauxels. (2019, November 5). *Group of people making toast.* Pexels. https://www.pexels.com/photo/group-of-people-making-toast-3184183/

Geralt. (2019, December 10). *Emotional intelligence eq iq.* Pixabay. https://pixabay.com/illustrations/emotional-intelligence-eq-iq-4682765/

Hannah, D. (2020, April 3). *Eye creative galaxy collage.* Pixabay. https://pixabay.com/illustrations/eye-creative-galaxy-collage-4997724/

Hassan, M. (2020, October 16). *Brain headphone music frequency*. Pixabay. https://pixabay.com/vectors/brain-headphone-music-frequency-5659627/

Piacquadio, A. (2018, March 3). *Close-Up photography of woman sleeping*. Pexels. https://www.pexels.com/photo/close-up-photography-of-woman-sleeping-914910/

Pixabay. (2016, February 4). *Woman with white sunvisor running*. Pexels. https://www.pexels.com/photo/woman-with-white-sunvisor-running-40751/

RF Studio. (2019, October 10). *Photo of woman doing meditation*. Pexels. https://www.pexels.com/photo/photo-of-woman-doing-meditation-3059892/

Roseclay, D. (2018, June 5). *Woman in grey top hugging brown dachshund*. Pexels. https://www.pexels.com/photo/woman-in-grey-top-hugging-brown-dachshund-1139793/

Sensei, N. (2019, June 28). *Two cups of coffee on table*. Pexels. https://www.pexels.com/photo/two-cups-of-coffee-on-table-2575835/

Sh, N. (2023, March 22). *Soup with fish*. Pexels. https://www.pexels.com/photo/soup-with-fish-16028788/

Shopify Partners. (n.d.). *Hand holds model brain photo*. Burst. https://burst.shopify.com/photos/hand-holds-model-brain?q=brain+structure

Simonproulx. (2021, January 20). *Mushrooms lion's mane fungi*. Pixabay. https://pixabay.com/photos/mushrooms-lion-s-mane-fungi-5929126/

Smith, K. (2017, August 8). *Woman holding her head*. Pexels. https://www.pexels.com/photo/woman-holding-her-head-551588/

Thesis. (2021, November 3). *Capsules in plastic containers with labels*. Pexels. https://www.pexels.com/photo/capsules-in-plastic-containers-with-labels-10132273/

Wallusy. (2019, September 24). *People talking gesturing*. Pixabay. https://pixabay.com/vectors/people-talking-gesturing-4498458/